MONOGRAPHS OF THE PHYSIOLOGICAL SOCIETY

Editors: H. Barcroft, H. Davson, W. D. M. Paton

Number 14 · PHYSIOLOGY OF THE
SPLANCHNIC CIRCULATION

MONOGRAPHS OF THE PHYSIOLOGICAL SOCIETY

Volumes marked * are now out of print

PHYSIOLOGY OF THE SPLANCHNIC CIRCULATION

by

J. GRAYSON

M.Sc., M.D.(V.U. Manc.), Ch.B.
Professor of Physiology, University of Ibadan, Nigeria

and

D. MENDEL

M.D.(London), M.R.C.P.
Reader in Physiology, King's College, London

LONDON
EDWARD ARNOLD (PUBLISHERS) LTD

1965

First published 1965

1570

17/9/79

Printed in Great Britain by
Butler & Tanner Ltd, Frome and London

PREFACE

THIS work is intended to deal primarily with physiological problems associated with the circulation in the gastro-intestinal tract, spleen and liver. It is hard to find a concise designation describing accurately this precise vascular territory. "Visceral" is a phrase covering too wide a ground; "splanchnic" (from the Greek *splagkhna*—entrails) is preferred. Even this description falls short of semantic perfection; its employment in the present context is, however, in part hallowed by usage and, in any case, is justified by the lack of anything better.

The gastro-intestinal tract, spleen and liver form a triad of organs whose pivot, so to speak, is the portal vein. The portal vein is essentially an accessory of metabolism necessary for the transport of absorbed products; it is the direct link between gut, spleen and liver. Yet, functionally linked though they may be, from the standpoint of their circulatory reactions the structures involved in the splanchnic circulation are very different.

There is, unfortunately, one gap in both this and most other reviews of splanchnic vascular reactions, namely, the pancreatic circulation. It is omitted from this work since the available information is too scanty to enable it to be considered in relation to the rest of the portal circulation.

Despite the multiplicity of methods applied to the problem of measurement within the bowel circulation, it will be evident that there is still a regrettable lack of any completely satisfactory quantitative approach both in animals and in man. The inaccessibility of the bowel and its anatomy are the real problems. Meanwhile, from the physiological point of view, although the bowel circulation is invoked widely in the aetiology of such diverse conditions as gastric ulcer and traumatic shock, it remains a sadly neglected field.

This apart, the splanchnic circulation forms a remarkable epitome of the peripheral circulation as a whole. There are the contrasting demands of local functional and nutritional needs and the demands on the splanchnic region of blood pressure regulation—which implies not merely resistance adjustments but also involves complex blood storage functions. There are, added to all this, the unique problems created by the portal vein.

From the point of view of the vascular physiologist the whole portal system is inelegant to a degree, a vascular absurdity. The secondary problems of circulatory control, created by the demands of functional unity, are highly involved. Yet in the living body they are solved by as remarkable an arrangement of physiological compromises as could well be considered.

It is the consideration of these physiological compromises that forms the main purpose of the present work.

Acknowledgement of permission to reproduce published figures is due to the authors of the papers and to the Editors of the following Journals:

> *American Journal of Anatomy*
> *American Journal of Physiology*
> *Anatomical Records*
> *British Medical Journal*
> *Circulation Research*
> *Clinical Science*
> *Journal of Pharmacology*
> *Journal of Physiology*
> *Lancet*
> *Physiological Reviews*
> *Surgery, Gynaecology and Obstetrics*

We are also grateful to Longmans, Green and Co. Ltd. for permission to reproduce figures 1.1, 1.2 and 1.6.

CONTENTS

ANATOMY OF THE SPLANCHNIC CIRCULATION

Arterial blood supply

The splanchnic area in the mammal receives its arterial blood supply from a series of closely interconnected vessels; the coeliac artery, the superior mesenteric artery and the inferior mesenteric artery. The coeliac artery is a short, wide vessel arising from the aorta just below the diaphragm. It divides into three branches, the left gastric, hepatic and splenic arteries (Fig. 1.1).

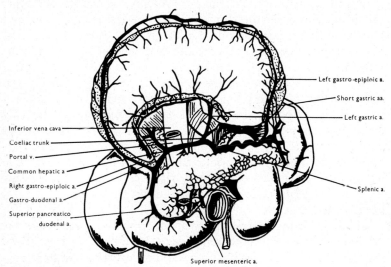

Left gastro-epiploic a.

Short gastric aa.

Left gastric a.

Inferior vena cava

Coeliac trunk

Portal v.

Common hepatic a

Right gastro-epiploic a.

Gastro-duodenal a.

Superior pancreatico-
duodenal a.

Splenic a.

Superior mesenteric a.

FIG. 1.1. The coeliac trunk and its branches in man exposed by turning the stomach upwards and removing the peritoneum on the posterior abdominal wall.

(From *Gray's Anatomy*.)

The left gastric artery supplies part of the stomach along the lesser curvature, and through these branches anastomoses with branches of the splenic artery and the right gastric artery. At the cardiac end of the stomach it gives off two or three oesophageal arteries, which anastomose with aortic oesophageal arteries.

The hepatic artery provides the main source of arterial blood for the liver. In the porta hepatis it divides into right and left branches which supply the corresponding lobes of the liver. It gives off the right gastric artery, which runs along the lesser curvature of the stomach and anastomoses with the left gastric artery, and the gastroduodenal artery which divides into the right gastro-epiploic and superior pancreaticoduodenal arteries. The cystic artery arises from the right branch of the hepatic artery. Through these vessels the stomach, pancreas, duodenum and gall bladder are supplied. The liver can receive additional blood supply through the "bare area" from the phrenic arteries. This has been shown by Segall (1923) for man, and by Jefferson, Proffit and Necheles (1952) for the dog.

The splenic artery is the main source of supply to the spleen, but it also gives rise to numerous small pancreatic arteries, the short gastric arteries and the left gastro-epiploic artery. The short gastric arteries enter the stomach along the lesser curvature, and anastomose with branches of the left gastric artery and the left gastro-epiploic artery. There are also anastomoses between the left and right gastro-epiploic arteries.

The superior mesenteric artery arises from the aorta below the coeliac artery. It gives rise to the inferior pancreaticoduodenal artery which supplies the pancreas and duodenum, and then by means of some twelve to fifteen jejunal and ileal branches supplies the jejunum and ileum. The superior mesenteric artery also supplies the caecum, ascending colon and most of the transverse colon by means of the ileocolic artery, right colic and middle colic arteries. The right colic artery anastomoses with the ileocolic and middle colic arteries.

The inferior mesenteric artery arises from the aorta below the origin of the superior mesenteric artery. By means of superior and inferior left colic arteries it supplies the terminal part of the transverse colon, the whole of the descending colon and the pelvic colon; and by its continuation as the superior rectal artery supplies part of the rectum. There it anastomoses with branches from the internal iliac artery. A connection between the superior and inferior mesenteric supplies occurs through anastomoses between the middle colic and superior left colic arteries. Variations in the arterial supply to the splanchnic area in man have been fully described by Michels (1955).

A remarkable feature of the arterial supply to the small intestine and colon is the formation of arcades freely communicating one with the other and from which arise the short arteries of supply (vasa recta) to the gut wall. This provides a blood supply dependent on no single source and often capable of adequate functioning even in the presence of damage or kinking. The intestinal blood supply of different species has been examined by Noer (1943). In man there are three or four series of arcades, and the vasa recta do not communicate with each other. In the dog, rhesus monkey, cat and guinea pig there are only primary and secondary arcades in close proximity to the gut wall, and there are abundant vasa recta communications. The dog intestine has thicker wall and an abundant capillary bed which Noer suggests makes it difficult to produce bowel ischaemia. The rabbit has a less complex arcuate system than man, but the vasa recta are similar.

Venous drainage

The veins of the gastro-intestinal tract drain into a series of arcades in close anatomical proximity to the arterial arcades. From these arcades drain a number of collecting veins. Those draining the small intestine, caecum, ascending and transverse colon converge on the superior mesenteric vein. Those draining the remainder of the colon and the rectum converge on the inferior mesenteric vein (Fig. 1.2). The splenic vein drains the spleen and is joined by a number of tributaries from the stomach (short gastric veins), pancreas and omentum. Douglass, Bagenstross and Hollinshead (1950) have shown that in man, the short gastric veins frequently enter the superior portion of the spleen. The largest tributary of the splenic vein is the inferior mesenteric vein which joins it not far from its termination. The portal vein is formed by the junction of the splenic and superior mesenteric veins. It is a short vein—about 8 cm long in man—which enters the porta hepatis in company with the hepatic artery and the bile duct. Within the porta hepatis it divides into right and left branches which accompany the corresponding branches of the hepatic artery into the substance of the liver. The right branch enters the right lobe of the liver, the left branch—longer but of smaller calibre than the right —gives branches to the caudate and quadrate lobes, then enters the left lobe of the liver. The portal vein receives the left gastric veins, which drain both surfaces of the stomach along the lesser curvature and receives some oesophageal veins. It receives the right gastric vein which drains the region of the pylorus, the cystic vein which drains the gall bladder and ends in the right branch of the portal vein. It also receives the umbilical veins, which run from the umbilicus in the ligamentum teres and end in the left branch of the portal vein, thereby establishing an anastomoses between the veins of the anterior abdominal wall and the portal vein.

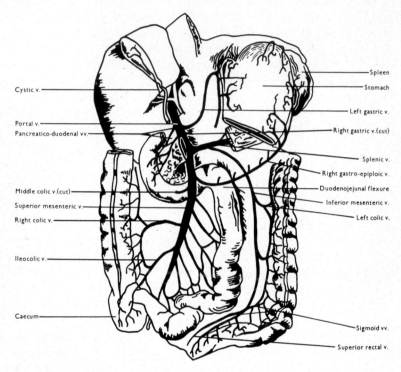

FIG. 1.2. The portal vein and its tributaries in man. Portions of the stomach, pancreas and the left lobe of the liver have been removed together with the transverse colon.

(From *Gray's Anatomy*.)

The detailed distribution of the portal system within the liver will be described later (Chapter V). For the present it is necessary to state that it divides into the interlobular veins from which arises the sinusoidal system in turn draining into the centrilobular veins. These join and finally form the hepatic veins which form the main venous return of the splanchnic system. There are two main groups of hepatic veins, the upper group being the larger.

They empty into the vena cava at about the level of the

diaphragm. There are no valves in the hepatic veins. The question of venous sphincters is considered later (Chapter V).

There are direct communications between the splanchnic and systemic venous systems. They have been classified by McIndoe (1928). The most important of these communications are those which occur at the lower end of the oesophagus between the branches of the left gastric vein and the oesophageal veins, and those which occur in the mucosa of the rectum through the superior middle and inferior rectal veins. There are others which are more variable; the para-umbilical veins which join the portal vein to the umbilical veins; the accessory portal system of Sappey, branches of which pass in the round and falciform ligaments to unite epigastric and internal mammary veins; the veins of Retzius which connect the retro-peritoneal surfaces of abdominal viscera with the inferior vena cava. Edwards (1951) has emphasized the importance of the retro-peritoneal veins and has shown that the communications are normally patent, whereas the para-umbilical veins are only patent in cases of portal obstruction. Variations in the venous drainage of the splanchnic region have been described by Douglass, Bagenstross and Hollinshead (1950).

The microcirculation

The anatomy of the microcirculation deriving from the vascular arcades in the gastro-intestinal tract has been beautifully demonstrated in the work of Barlow (1951) and Barlow, Bentley and Walder (1951). They used a variety of techniques—the injection of opaque media into human stomachs freshly removed at operation, followed by microradiography; the injection of coloured media, the sectioning and dissection of the specimens.

A striking observation which arose from this work is that there are no end-arteries in the accepted sense of the word (Fig. 1.3). There is in the first place an extensive submucous plexus of large vessels deriving directly from the arterial chains on the lesser and greater curvatures of the stomach. From this complex network arise the mucosal arteries (which can in some situations arise directly from the externally situated chains). These, too, anastomose freely with each other as they approach the muscularis mucosa —and again on the glandular aspect of that layer. It is from this plexus of small arteries that the remarkably rich capillary bed arises.

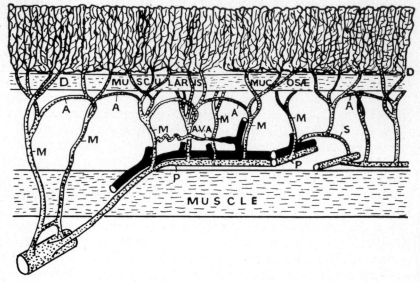

FIG. 1.3. Diagram of the vascular arrangement in the stomach wall of man. The mucosal arteries M arise from the left gastric artery outside the stomach wall.

A—Anastomosis between two mucosal arteries.
D—Network in glandular aspect of muscularis mucosae from which
    capillaries of mucosa arise.
AVA—Arterio-venous anastomosis.
P—Submucous plexus.
S—Subsidiary anastomotic channels.

(From Barlow, Bentley and Walder, 1951.)

Arterio-venous anastomoses

The discovery of profuse and functionally important arterio-venous anastomoses in the skin (Grant and Bland, 1931) and rabbit ear (Clark and Clark, 1934) gave impetus to a re-examination of the whole question of arterio-venous anastomoses elsewhere. Whereas previously they had been associated with specialized structures only, such as erectile tissues, it now appeared that they might have a wider functional significance. Two types of arterio-venous anastomoses were recognized; the direct type consisting of long straight channels connecting artery and vein ("expanded capillary type"), the other was the glomus type in which the long connecting channel had a tortuous and complicated course (Schumacher, 1938).

De Busscher (1948) was the first to describe the occurrence of "glomus" forms of arterio-venous communications in all layers of the stomach except the mucosa. Subsequent work has failed to confirm his findings in detail; nevertheless, there can be no doubt that arterio-venous anastomoses do exist in the submucous coat of the stomach at least. The work of Barclay and Bentley (1949) and of Barlow (1951) has revealed the presence of large numbers of anastomotic channels arising mainly from the mucosal arteries and running short courses to empty into the mucosal veins (Fig. 1.4).

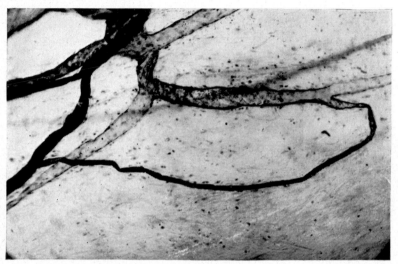

FIG. 1.4. Arterio-venous anastomosis in submucosa of human stomach (×15). Arteries dark. Veins light.

(Kind permission of Dr. Barlow.)

The details vary, but in the main they are 1 to 2 mm in length and not less than 30 μ in diameter in fixed specimens. Barlow, Bentley and Walder (1951) perfused isolated human stomachs with oxygenated plasma or human blood containing glass spheres between 40 and 200 μ in diameter. These spheres were too large to pass through capillaries and their appearance in the venous outflow was taken as further evidence for the existence of patent arterio-venous anastomoses.

It has been stated that arterio-venous anastomoses exist in the intestinal villi of man (Sparrow, 1932) and in the large intestine (Thamm, 1940). Brockis and Moffat (1958) consider their presence in the colon as not proven. Boulter and Parks (1959), however, have found a few arterio-venous anastomoses in the submucosal layer of the colon. They were 30–35 μ in diameter and were described as being of the expanded capillary type.

Metarterioles and vasomotion

The work of Chambers and Zweifach (1944) in describing met-arterioles and vasomotion is well established. The anatomical basis for their conceptions arose from observations of the detailed micro-circulation in the mesentery of the rat. The classical picture of the microcirculation pictures an arteriole with contractile elements in its coat, subdividing into precapillaries, which subdivide in turn to form capillaries proper. The capillaries become venous capillaries which join to form venules and then veins.

The configuration described by Chambers and Zweifach is shown in Fig. 1.5. A long loop arises from an arteriole and finally

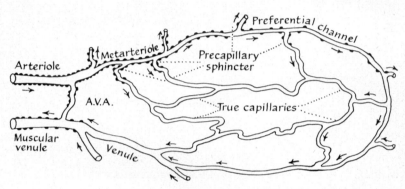

FIG. 1.5. Schematic representation of the structural pattern of the capillary bed in the mesentery of the rat. The distribution of smooth muscle is indicated in the vessel wall. Simple arterio-venous anastomoses are also shown—AVA.

(From Zweifach, 1949.)

ends in a venule. This loop in its early post-arteriolar stage is termed the metarteriole. It contains in its wall many smooth muscle fibres. Arising from it are the precapillaries. These do not contain smooth muscle and are regarded as non-contractile, though at their origins there is a sphincter-like thickening of the smooth muscle of the metarteriole. The precapillaries give rise to the true capillaries—thin endothelial lined tubes, again regarded by Chambers and Zweifach as non-contractile. The metarteriole continues as a central or preferential channel (still containing smooth muscle) and finally empties into a venule. The venous capillaries join together and either empty into a venule directly, or more usually, empty into the more distal portions of the preferential channel.

Anatomically this arrangement differs from the classical picture in that smooth muscle is found beyond the arterioles, the pre-capillaries are controlled by the sphincters at their origins and the whole complex forms a single vascular unit. This system also provides the anatomical basis for sequestration of blood in the mesentery since contraction of the preferential channel distally prevents venous blood from reaching the venule and converts the whole unit into a vascular reservoir controlled by a sort of "sluice" which is the distal portion of the preferential channel.

The metarterioles appear to be the main controlling units of the mesenteric capillary bed. They undergo, independently of each other and apparently at random, slow rhythmic movements so that circulatory units are periodically flushed with blood. Under conditions of high blood flow the periods of relaxation of the metarterioles and its sphincters are prolonged, and under conditions of reduced blood flow the periods of closure are prolonged.

Functionally, the main importance of this work lies not so much in the anatomical description—for metarterioles as such have never been demonstrated in other tissues—but in the dynamic concept of vascular tone. The probability is that vasomotion is a widespread phenomenon. It can be seen in the capillary circulation of the nail bed; something rather like it has been recorded in rat liver (Knisely, 1939). It is based on the concept of a vascular unit—consisting of an arteriole and all its precapillary and capillary branches. In living tissue this unit undergoes a constant cyclic activity moving from the fully open state when blood flow through the unit is maximum to the fully closed state when blood flow is zero. In any tissue total blood flow will depend on the number of open channels at any one time. The isolated perfused tissue has a rate of vasomotion which determines the passive blood flow for that perfusion pressure. In so far as it leads to an increase in blood flow a further decrease in the rate of vasomotion is equivalent to what was previously termed vasodilatation; in so far as it leads to a decrease in blood flow an increase in the rate of vasomotion is equivalent to vasoconstriction. This approach to vascular tone makes it no longer necessary to visualize active vasodilatation as a mechanism whereby blood vessels increase their diameter beyond the relaxed state—always a difficult concept; nor to visualize vascular tone as a fixed "setting" of vessel diameter. Vascular tone is now a mean rate of vasomotion and blood flow through a tissue is now determined by the overall activity of its constituent vascular units.

Nevertheless we shall retain the phrases "vasoconstriction" and "vasodilatation" partly for convenience and partly because, looked at as an expression of mean vessel diameter at any one time, even in terms of vasomotion, they are still accurate.

The nerve supply of the splanchnic circulation

Sympathetic innervation

The entire gastro-intestinal region down to the descending colon is supplied from the thoracic sympathetic outflow from Thoracic 5 to Thoracic 12. The remainder of the colon and rectum derive their supply from the lumbar outflow Lumbar 1–Lumbar 3.

The thoracic sympathetic supply to the gastro-intestinal tract,

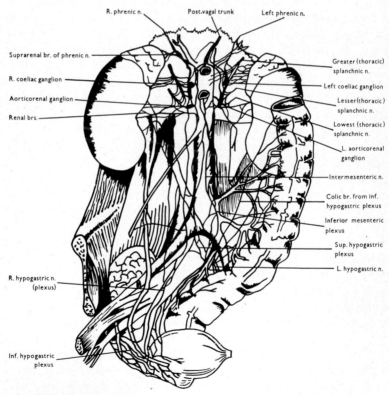

Fig. 1.6. Autonomic nerves and plexuses in the abdomen and pelvis of man.

(From *Gray's Anatomy*—after G. A. G. Mitchell.)

liver and spleen is gathered into three principal paired nerves, the greater, the lesser and the lowest splanchnic or renal nerve (Fig. 1.6). These nerves are composed of myelinated pre-ganglionic fibres which arise in the first place from the lateral columns of grey cell in the spinal cord, emerge in the white rami communicans, and pass directly through the relevant sympathetic ganglia without relaying (Ranson and Billingsley, 1918). The largest nerve is the greater splanchnic which is common to many mammalia. It is formed by branches of the 5th to 9th thoracic sympathetic ganglia (Ranson, 1935) and descends obliquely upon the bodies of the vertebrae, perforates the crus of the diaphragm, and ends in the coeliac ganglion, which is found on the vertebral bodies of the last thoracic and 1st lumbar vertebrae. The lesser splanchnic is a very much smaller trunk composed of fibres from Thoracic 9 and 10 sympathetic ganglia, and sometimes Thoracic 11. It pierces the diaphragm with the greater splanchnic nerve and ends in the aorticorenal ganglion which is connected to the coeliac ganglion. The lowest splanchnic nerve arises from the 12th thoracic ganglion and runs a separate course to enter the renal plexus. Within the abdominal cavity is a complex of nerve plexuses and ganglia which supply the viscera and blood vessels with their entire sympathetic post-ganglionic non-myelinated innervation.

SYMPATHETIC SUPPLY TO INDIVIDUAL ORGANS

Liver

The distribution of the sympathetic supply to the liver has been summarized by Lewis (1951). The fibres arise from the anterior and posterior hepatic plexus. The anterior hepatic plexus lies in close association with the hepatic artery and arises from the left coeliac ganglion. The fibres supply the gall bladder and cystic duct. The posterior hepatic plexus lies on the posterior aspect of the portal vein and arises from the right coeliac ganglion, the origin of the fibres being Thoracic 7–10. The posterior plexus receives a branch from the anterior plexus and the fibres accompany the arteries and bile ducts throughout the liver. The arteries are said to be exclusively innervated by the sympathetics. In addition, the right phrenic plexus, which arises from the upper part of the coeliac ganglion and accompanies the inferior phrenic artery, receives one or two branches from the right phrenic nerve. Fibres from this plexus are also distributed to the liver.

Spleen

The sympathetic supply to the spleen arises mainly from the left coeliac plexus (Glaser, 1928; Riegele, 1929) in the pig, dog and cat. In the cat and rat the fibres form a plexus on the splenic artery extending to the hilum of the spleen. Some of the fibres enter the capsule. The unmyelinated fibres within the spleen reach their terminal destinations in the red pulp in association with arterial branches, and along the smallest venous tributaries and associated trabeculae. Some of these fibres terminate in intimate relation to contractile cells in the walls of the smallest vessels (Utterback, 1944). Cleland and Tait (1927) described in the dog and cat two bands of nerve fibres along the splenic artery, one of which they suggest innervated arteries within the spleen and the other the smooth muscle elements within the capsule and the trabeculae. They also described non-medullated sympathetic fibres which leave the cord at the level of the 6th cervical foramen, run with the left phrenic nerve into the abdomen and then supply the splenic vein. Kuntze and Jacobs (1955) have demonstrated sympathetic nerve fibres in the cat and rat which pass through the coeliac ganglion and relay more peripherally in ganglia along the course of the splenic artery. They may occasionally be found in the dog (see Daly and Scott, 1961).

Gastro-intestinal tract

The sympathetic supply to the stomach is mainly from the coeliac plexus through the plexuses around the gastric and gastro-epiploic arteries (Mitchell, 1940), but fibres also arise from the hepatic plexus and the left phrenic plexus. Nerve plexuses occur in the submucous coat (Meissner's plexus) and between the layers of the muscular coat (Auerbach's plexus). Fibres pass from here to the muscular tissue and the mucous membrane. The small intestine receives a sympathetic innervation from the coeliac ganglia and plexuses around the superior mesenteric artery. Fibres are distributed from Auerbach's plexus to the muscle and mucosa. The caecum, appendix, ascending colon and the right two-thirds of the transverse colon receive their sympathetic supply from the coeliac and mesenteric ganglia. The nerves are distributed to the gut by plexuses around branches of the superior mesenteric artery. The remainder of the large intestine and rectum are innervated from the lumbar sympathetic and the hypogastric plexus by means of the plexuses on the branches of the inferior mesenteric artery. The terminal distribution to the large bowel is similar to that in the small intestine.

Parasympathetic innervation

The vagus supplies the whole of the splanchnic area down to the right two-thirds of the transverse colon. The fibres supplying the splanchnic area arise from the dorsal nucleus of the vagus and are distributed through the coeliac, gastric and hepatic plexuses to the abdominal organs. The fibres supplying the gastro-intestinal tract relay in Auerbach's and Meissner's plexus and fibres are distributed to glands and muscle. The parasympathetic supply to the remainder of the colon and rectum is by the nervi erigentes from sacral segments 2 and 3 (Mitchell, 1935).

The innervation of blood vessels by vagal fibres is far from certain. Letnik-Satyukova (1951) claims to have established by "direct observation" that the motor plexuses of gastric arteries contain small branches from the ganglia of Auerbach's plexus. According to Lewis (1951) the left vagus in man which joins the hepatic plexus from the left coeliac ganglion is distributed to the gall bladder and bile duct but not to the hepatic vasculature. Mikhail and Saleh (1961) have studied the nerve supply to the parenchyma of the liver in the rat, mouse, guinea pig, rabbit and dog. The parenchyma was found to be richly supplied with nerve fibres. Terminal parasympathetic ganglia were found. Dendrites and post-ganglionic fibres interlaced together forming a terminal plexus in the liver parenchyma. In connection with the spleen, Glaser (1928) found that some vagal fibres join the plexus along the splenic artery from the left coeliac plexus, which were, however, probably pre-ganglionic to the pancreas. No ganglion cells in the spleen have been described and Utterback (1944) could find no evidence of vagal innervation of the spleen in cats or rats when examined by section of the vagi.

HAEMODYNAMIC CONSIDERATIONS IN THE
SPLANCHNIC CIRCULATION

FROM the haemodynamic point of view it is convenient to consider three divisions of the splanchnic blood supply. Fig. 2.1 illustrates

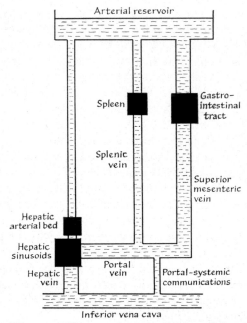

FIG. 2.1. Diagram to illustrate the main divisions of the splanchnic circulation. System divisible into three different pressure zones— (a) Fluctuating pressure head supplying three main parallel resistances: namely, gastro-intestinal, splenic and hepatic arterial. (b) Intermediate pressure zone in the portal vein and its tributaries. (c) Low pressure zone in the hepatic vein and outlet system beyond hepatic sinusoids.

The direct portal–systematic connections are also represented.

the problem. The arterial reservoir indicated may be regarded as a pulsatile pressure head from which the blood drains through three parallel resistances, gastro-intestinal, splenic and hepatic.

The outflow from the gastro-intestinal and splenic components constitute the major inflow to the portal vein.

Each of the resistance circuits has special features. The gastro-intestinal tract is complicated by the presence of arterio-venous anastomoses, by the localization of vessels in the walls of viscera which may change their intramural tension and so alter blood flow, by its own demands for blood during digestive activity and by its contribution to overall changes in peripheral vascular resistance and shifts of blood volume. With the spleen there is the possibility of an open circulation into the splenic pulp and the function of blood storage. The hepatic artery has fine terminals emptying directly into the liver sinusoids and is a determinant of portal inflow. The principal route for the return of blood from the splanchnic circulation to the systemic circulation is by the hepatic veins draining into the inferior vena cava. The veins may, in some species, have a sphincter. The storage of blood in the liver and the possibility of drainage of intestinal blood through patent retro-peritoneal connections with the vena cava must also be considered. Bradley (1958) has emphasized that "a full knowledge of the distribution and volume of flows within different parts of the bed and of pressure gradients is required for the interpretation of changes at any single point. . . . Pressure or flow in any portion—the portal vein for example—is dependent upon the system as a whole."

Before considering these overall considerations in detail there are, however, certain general concepts in connection with pressure and flow which should be considered.

Pressure, flow and resistance

A simple association of pressure, flow and resistance can be defined by analogy to Ohm's law as $F = P/R$, where F is the flow, P the pressure and R is the vascular resistance in arbitrary units. Resistance to flow can arise from active changes in the smooth muscle of the vascular bed, from passive changes in geometry of the vascular bed and from changes in the viscosity of the blood. Some physical laws derived from haemodynamics have been applied to blood flow and these will be discussed.

Poiseuille's law

This law was derived from a study of flow in rigid tubes (Poiseuille, 1830). It may be simply stated as

$$F = (P_1 - P_2) . \left(\frac{\pi r^4}{8L}\right) . \frac{1}{V}$$

where F is the flow, P_1 and P_2 the pressures at the ends of the tube, r the radius, L the length and V the viscosity of the fluid. If we compare this with the formula for Ohm's law, vascular resistance can be expressed as

$$R = \frac{P}{F} = \left(\frac{8L}{\pi r^4}\right) \cdot \frac{V}{1}$$

Poiseuille's law, therefore, enables us to evaluate two of the major factors in vascular resistance, namely viscosity and the dimensions of the vasculature.

In the system used by Poiseuille, the viscosity of the fluid and geometry of the tube were constant. A plot of flow versus pressure gives a straight line through the origin and one of resistance versus pressure a horizontal straight line (Fig. 2.2).

Effect of anomalous viscosity and of
distensibility on $F-P$ and $R-P$ curves

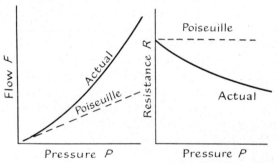

FIG. 2.2. To illustrate deviations from Poiseuille's law when living blood vessels are perfused with blood. (After Burton, 1952.)

The flow–pressure curves obtained with blood in vascular beds are, however, quite different from those obtained with rigid tubes (Fig. 2.2). The curves do not pass through the origin and there is a fall in resistance with increasing pressure. The shape of the curve depends upon the tone in the vessels and on the viscosity of the blood. The curves for dilated vessels are almost linear; with increasing tone the curves are sigmoid and convex to the flow axis. Flow–pressure curves for the rabbit ear, in which tone has been altered by different degrees of sympathetic stimulation, are shown in Fig. 2.3.

Deviations from Poiseuille's law could arise if (1) blood showed anomalous viscosity, a concept which suggests that viscosity alters

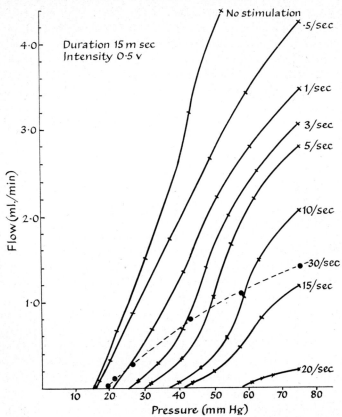

FIG. 2.3. Pressure–flow curves for the rabbit ear with different frequencies of stimulation of the cervical sympathetic ganglion. This
shows "critical closing", i.e. zero flow with a positive perfusion pressure. It also shows higher levels of critical closing pressure when
neurogenic vascular tone was increased.

(After Burton, 1952.)

with driving pressure, and (2) if the geometric factor varies due
to distensibility of blood vessels. Anomalous viscosity of blood
arises from the tendency for red cells to concentrate in the axial
stream, a phenomenon depending upon the velocity of blood in
different portions of the cross-sectional area of a blood vessel. The
most peripheral layer of blood will tend to cling to the vessel and
at its extreme boundary will remain motionless. The layer next to
the most peripheral will have a forward velocity but will be retarded by the viscous drag of the outer layers. As the centre of the
vessel is approached the velocity will be greatest, since it is retarded

by a layer which itself has a forward motion. The effect of the accumulation of red cells in the centre of the vessel is to diminish the viscosity. The tendency for axial streaming to occur will increase with decreasing calibre of vessel and with increase in driving pressure. It has been shown that the viscosity of blood flowing through rigid tubes is reduced with vessel diameters of 300 μ down to 14 μ (Bayliss, 1952).

Some workers, however, doubt the importance of anomalous viscosity in explaining the shape of the flow–pressure curves in biological systems. Whittaker and Winton (1933) found in perfusion experiments with the hind limb of the dog, that the apparent changes in viscosity with pressure were less than would have been expected. Haynes and Burton (1959) have found from perfusion of fine glass tubes with different erythrocyte suspensions, that the flow properties were linear over the physiological range and that axial streaming reaches its maximum at a relatively low rate of flow. Burton (1959) has found that the relationship between pressure and flow in a perfused vascular bed was similar with blood or Ringer's solution as the perfusate.

Nevertheless there is a growing body of opinion which thinks otherwise (McComis, Charm and Kurland, 1964). The recent interest in rheological studies as applied to the flow of blood in tubes leaves little doubt that Poiseuille's law does not apply to perfusion of glass capillaries with non-Newtonian fluids such as blood. There is a tendency to discard the phrase "anomalous viscosity" and there have been a number of attempts to restate the mathematics underlying the flow of non-Newtonian fluids without assuming any actual change in viscosity. There is little doubt that the physical properties of blood are an important determinant of blood flow. Unfortunately the present state of rheological knowledge does not greatly help in the interpretation of macrophysiological problems.

Blood vessels and blood flow

In addition to the problems posed by the fact that blood is a viscous fluid is the fact that in the living body blood flows through a complex and distensible system of vessels. A number of attempts have been made to determine the underlying factors.

The importance of the distensibility of blood vessels in the explanation of pressure and flow curves in biological preparations has been emphasized by Burton (1959). The vessel wall contains three elements in relation to distension. The elastic tissue, which takes up the distension initially, the collagenous fibres which resist greater degrees of distension, and the smooth muscle which has contractile properties relatively independent of stretch. Roach and Burton (1957) have explained the shape of the pressure–flow curves by determining equations for the physical equilibrium of a cylinder under these conditions.

Critical closure

It has been mentioned that pressure–flow curves in perfused biological systems do not pass through the origin (Fig. 2.3), so that flow is not appreciable until a critical pressure is reached. This pressure has been termed "critical closing pressure" by Burton (1951). An explanation of the phenomenon has been given by Burton in terms of the equilibrium of small blood vessels. It has been shown by LaPlace (1841) that the tension (T) in the wall of a cylinder of radius r, is equal to the distending pressure P multiplied by the radius, that is $T = Pr$. The distending pressure in the lumen is equal to the inside pressure minus the tissue pressure and may be termed the transmural pressure.

The factors contributing to tension in the wall of the vessel are, however, complex. They include an elasticity factor contributed by the elastic components at normal pressures and by collagenous fibres at high pressures. They also include a factor contributed by the tension of smooth muscle which itself depends on vasomotor tone. If the elastic factor alone were to be considered the relation between transmural pressure and vessel diameter would probably be linear according to LaPlace's law. The existence of smooth muscle factors, however, generate instabilities at low pressure which lead to complete closure whilst the transmural pressure is still positive. The actual value of the closing pressure (the critical closing pressure of Burton) is, in consequence, a function of muscle tone (Fig. 2.3).

In relation to the splanchnic circulation, critical closing pressures of 16 mm Hg have been found in the perfused intestine of the dog (Selkurt, Scibetta and Cull, 1958), 7–13 cm of plasma in the rat liver perfused through the portal vein (Brauer, Leong, McElroy and Holloway, 1955), and 20 mm Hg in rat liver perfused through the hepatic artery (Grayson and Mendel, 1957a).

Another important aspect of Burton's concepts is that since elastic tissue is important in allowing a graded constriction or dilatation in the blood vessel wall when changes in active wall tension occur due to smooth muscle, it would be expected that vessels without elastic tissue would be either fully open or fully closed, a feature which probably applies to arterio-venous shunts and precapillary sphincters.

Passive and active changes in resistance

In studies of the peripheral circulation it is useful to measure peripheral resistance. Vascular resistance can be calculated from the expression:

$$\text{Resistance} = \text{perfusion pressure/flow}$$

In the mesentery, the perfusion pressure is the systemic arteria pressure less the portal pressure.

In the portal circulation the perfusion pressure is the portal pressure less hepatic venous pressure.

In the hepatic arterial circulation the perfusion pressure is hepatic arterial pressure less the hepatic venous pressure.

The point has already been made that for practical purposes changes in resistance can be accounted for by changes in the geometry of the vascular bed. The geometry of the vascular bed can be affected by a number of factors, such as opening of capillary beds with changes in metabolism, by extra-vascular compression, by mechanical dilatation with rising perfusion pressure and by changes in the state of active contraction of smooth muscle through vasomotor nerves and humoral substances. The fact that passive changes in the calibre of a blood vessel can occur with changes in perfusion pressure makes it difficult to interpret changes in resistance in terms of active constriction or dilatation. Pressure/flow studies on isolated dog intestine (Selkurt *et al.*, 1958) with a range of pressure varying from 0 to 240 mm Hg gave a curvilinear relationship convex to the pressure axis, with both blood and dextran. Calculations of resistance showed a fall with rising perfusion pressure (Fig. 2.4). Similar relationships have been found for the isolated rat liver perfused through the portal vein with whole blood of plasma (Brauer *et al.*, 1955) and for the perfused dog spleen (Frohlich and Gillenwater, 1963).

The non-linear relationship of these pressure/flow curves means that active changes in resistance can be inferred when blood pressure is constant and a flow change occurs or when flow is constant and a pressure change occurs, or when flow and pressure change in opposite directions. When pressure and flow change in the same direction changes in active resistance cannot be deduced unless the passive changes in resistance produced by similar changes in these variables is known.

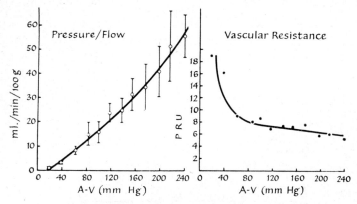

FIG. 2.4. Dog intestine. Relation between flow, vascular resistance and perfusion pressure showing "critical closing" and a fall in resistance with rising perfusion pressure.

(Selkurt, Scibetta and Cull, 1958.)

NERVOUS CONTROL OF VASOMOTOR TONE

It is convenient to consider briefly the various ways in which nervous activity can affect vasomotor tone. Fig. 2.5 shows a vessel wall with its possible nerve supplies. The account which follows is based on the receptor theory of Ahlquist (1948). According to this theory there are three types of receptor in the vessel wall, designated α, β and γ. The α receptor is innervated by adrenergic sympathetic nerve fibres and will cause constriction of the smooth muscle when stimulated by adrenaline or noradrenaline. The β receptor will cause dilatation of smooth muscle and is not innervated. It will respond to adrenaline and isoprenaline but not noradrenaline. The γ receptor is innervated by cholinergic sympathetic fibres, and will cause dilatation which can be prevented by atropine. Adrenaline can thus act through the α receptor to cause constriction and through the β receptor to cause dilatation. It is considered that β receptors have a lower threshold than α receptors so that small doses of adrenaline will only act on β receptors and cause dilatation, but that large doses of adrenaline will act on α receptors and obscure the effect of β receptors. Most vessels have α receptors but need not have β or γ receptors.

The term "vasodilatation" could, in these terms, have two connotations. The first is passive, that is a release of vasoconstrictor tone so that the vessel approaches a passive diameter in relation

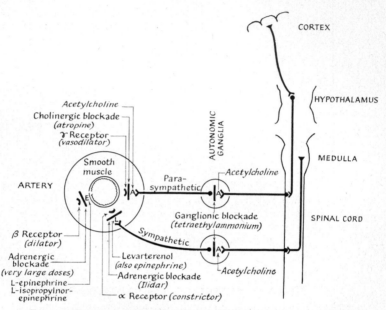

Fig. 2.5. Schematic diagram of the various receptors in the smooth muscle of the wall of a blood vessel (α, β, γ) and of the autonomic ganglion synapses. Illustrating, also, the site at which adrenergic and ganglionic blocking drugs act.

(After Green and Kepchar, 1959.)

to its internal pressure. The second is active, meaning that the diameter reached is greater still and the vessel tone reduced beyond the passive state.

AUTOREGULATION

The concept of autoregulation derives in the first instance from the observations of Shipley and Study (1951), who showed that renal blood flow was constant over a wide range of systemic arterial blood pressures (140 to 60 mm Hg). Moreover this constancy was independent of nervous or other extrinsic factors. Their findings suggested that resistance fell with diminished intravascular pressures, an observation which runs counter to the propositions given

above. Autoregulation, as the phenomenon is called, has subsequently been described in the liver (Ginsburg and Grayson,
1954), the brain (Carlyle and Grayson, 1956; Wasserman and
Patterson, 1961), in skeletal muscle (Folkow and Öberg, 1961) and
in the small intestine (Johnson, 1959).

When first described, the concept of autoregulation appeared to
lead to a view of circulatory control very different from previous
orthodox approaches. Thus it seemed that central control of the
circulation through the nervous system or endocrine mechanisms
was of little importance in many tissues such as the kidney, brain
and liver. In these tissues and probably others besides, local factors
were dominant and, although the blood vessels may have received
vasomotor innervations, the effects of enhanced or diminished
nervous activity were offset by the local effects of autoregulation.
Central control of the peripheral circulation was limited to its more
labile elements such as the skin.

Unfortunately the enthusiasm of its protagonists has not been
fully justified by further investigations into autoregulation. Nevertheless the weight of evidence is such that it is hard to avoid the
conclusion that autoregulation is a real phenomenon, and that there
is some lessening of vascular resistance in many vascular beds when
intravascular resistance falls. This does not mean that autoregulation is the dominant factor in circulatory control and there is considerable evidence to suggest that autoregulation is a variable
phenomenon. Failures to demonstrate it fully are almost as frequent
as reports of success (Alexander, 1963). Such factors as the degree
of operative trauma, haemorrhage, the depth of anaesthesia have
been shown to be important to the successful demonstration of
autoregulation (Ginsburg and Grayson, 1954; Schmid and Spencer,
1962; Johnson, 1959). Alexander (1963) states ". . . such reser-
vations are warnings that published records are likely to be best
records and the bias of the authors is likely to slant their evaluation
of data".

One view of autoregulation is to regard it as a property of vascular smooth muscle. It may be related to the property of all
muscle tissue, including vascular smooth muscle, to develop a
greater force of contraction with increase in stretch (Bayliss, 1902).
Folkow and Öberg (1961) give a substantial basis for the myogenic
view and claim that autoregulation is dependent upon the pre-
existence of a relatively normal degree of myogenic tone in the
vascular bed.

The present authors do not necessarily endorse Alexander's views to the full though it is clear that autoregulation is a variable phenomenon and probably depends on other factors as well as the nature of smooth muscle. One such factor is the physical property of blood itself. There may be other considerations, too, such as the reactions of vascular smooth muscle to relative anoxia. Its exact role in circulatory regulation remains to be determined and it will be discussed again more specifically in relation to the splanchnic circulation.

III

METHODS USED IN THE ASSESSMENT OF THE GASTRO-INTESTINAL CIRCULATION

THE measurement of flow of blood in tissues or vessels has been a fruitful field of physiological endeavour since the days of Harvey. To the present day, however, even the purely technological problems have never been satisfactorily solved. The information one can obtain from measurements of total flow into or out of an organ is useful but it is not the whole story concerning the blood flow within that organ. Ideally, techniques are required which will measure total flow, either directly on the vessels of supply or drainage or indirectly through some specific property of the tissue which can be measured and interpreted indirectly in terms of flow; techniques are also required which can assess quantitatively the distribution of blood within the organ and the patterns of flow response within the tissue substance. To be ideal such techniques should involve no trauma, no interference with the blood supply at any stage, they should be equally applicable to the conscious as to the unconscious animal and, of course, there should be no possibility of artefact and results should be capable of expression in absolute terms.

There is, of course, no single ideal general purpose technique although many ingenious methods have been brought to bear on individual aspects of blood flow problems.

MEASUREMENT OF FLOW IN CANNULATED VESSELS

(a) *Mechanical stromuhr*. The introduction of the mechanical stromuhr (Ludwig, 1867) enabled direct observations of flow to be made in the vessels supplying or draining the gut. The instrument was a flowmeter operating on simple mechanical principles, which could be connected by means of an ingoing and an outgoing cannula into the proximal and distal sections of a divided vessel. From the point of view of accuracy this instrument was satisfactory, its calibration was simple, and the results were absolute recordings of flow in ml. per minute. It had the disadvantages, however, of requiring an extensive operative procedure, flow along the vessel in question was totally interrupted for about 10 minutes and there was also imposed an artificial resistance to flow. The stromuhr was used to measure portal vein flow by Schmid (1908) and by Burton-Opitz (1911).

(*b*) *Direct measurement of venous outflow.* Barcroft and Shore (1912) cannulated a renal vein in the cat and directed the venous return from the lower part of the body through this cannula into a jugular or brachial vein. A second cannula was placed in the inferior vena cava below the liver. Clamping the vena cava above the liver now diverted the hepatic venous outflow through this cannula and enabled it to be measured directly. The contribution of the portal vein to this flow could be determined by clamping the hepatic artery. A similar technique has been used by MacLeod and Pearce (1914) and Blalock and Mason (1936). The venous outflow was measured by timing the collection of measured volumes of blood or, alternatively, by means of a drop counter. The venous outflow from the intestine has been similarly measured by Clark (1934) and Sidky and Bean (1958).

(*c*) *Bubble flow meters.* The mean rate of flow in arteries can be measured by timing the passage of an injected bubble of air through a tube of known length and volume which is placed between the cut ends of the vessel (Bruner, 1948). The bubble may be timed visually or photoelectrically (Selkurt, 1948). Because of the resistance to flow the bubble flow meter is only suitable for use in arteries. It has been used in studies of the intestinal and hepatic circulations by Cull, Scibetta and Selkurt (1956).

(*d*) *Rotameters.* This device consists of a vertical transparent tube within which the height of a float is determined by the rate of flow. The position of the float may be read visually or the vertical position of the float may be detected by an induction mechanism for continuous recording (Shipley and Wilson, 1951). There is little resistance to flow. They have been used in studies of the intestinal circulation by Selkurt and Johnson (1958).

(*e*) *Electromagnetic flowmeters.* The electromagnetic flowmeter (Kolin, 1936) has recently been used extensively in studies of the intestinal circulation (Ottis, Davis and Green, 1957; Green, Locksley, Hall, Sexton and Deal, 1959; Geber, 1960). The method depends upon the fact that a voltage is induced in a conductor moving through a magnetic field at right angles to the lines of

force. Blood serves as the conductor, the magnetic field is produced by a miniature electromagnet, and the induced voltage,
about one-millionth of a volt, is amplified and recorded. The
instrument can be used with cannulated or uncannulated vessels.
Its main advantages are that both mean and phasic flows can be
recorded from both large and small vessels, calibration is linear
and there is a high frequency response. Wyatt (1961) has discussed
the difficulties in using this type of flowmeter.

FLOW MEASUREMENT IN THE INTACT VESSEL

A technical advance which obviated altogether the disadvantages
of circulatory interruption and artificially imposed resistance was
the invention of the thermostromuhr by Rein (1928). Moreover,
the animal could be allowed to recover and observations made on
the intact conscious animal. This instrument, which could be
clipped on to an intact vessel, consisted of a heating element with
two thermocouples situated downstream. The temperature difference between the two thermocouples was recorded. With high
blood flows this difference was small, with low flows it was large.
Despite its many advantages, however, the method has received
critical attention from many workers. It is, without doubt, subject
to artefact. Local temperature changes or turbulence in the blood
vessels may seriously complicate the interpretation of the results
(Barcroft and Loughridge, 1938). Shipley, Gregg and Wearn (1942)
showed, too, that back flow in the vessels or even zero flow might
produce confusing pictures easily interpretable as forward flow.
Moreover, artefacts can easily arise from other causes such as
angulation of the unit, stretching of the artery, or movements of
extravascular fluid.

These criticisms notwithstanding, the method has been applied
by Rein and his co-workers with success (judged by the fact that
most of his results have subsequently been confirmed by other
methods), and by Grindlay, Herrick and Mann (1941). Successful
use of the method demands careful application of the apparatus at
operation and, above all, its application to vessels in which blood
flow is high.

The electromagnetic flowmeter has already been referred to. In
its first applications it was used with cannulated vessels. Recent
developments make it unnecessary to cannulate and it can be applied
to the intact vessel. Although its application requires operation the

animal can be allowed to recover and measurements made in the conscious animal. Thus far they appear to be free from most of the criticisms of the Rein thermostromuhr and in our present stage of technical development probably provide the most reliable of available techniques for the measurement of flow in intact vessels.

VOLUME MEASUREMENTS IN THE GASTRO-INTESTINAL TRACT

One of the earliest approaches to questions of gastro-intestinal circulation was the use of the plethysmograph for the measurement of gut volume. Bayliss (1893) made the first attempt at measurement, and Hallion and Francois-Franck (1896), Bunch (1899) and Bayliss and Starling (1899) used a plethysmograph successfully. The technique was later applied by Clark (1930) and Bülbring and Burn (1936). Volume changes in an organ can frequently be related to vascular events. They do not, however, distinguish between changes in through flow and changes in the amount of blood stored in the tissue. In the gastro-intestinal tract, blood storage function may well be important and this should be borne in mind in the interpretation of any volume change. The method can only be applied to the anaesthetized animal and involves manipulation of the intestines with the possibility of some constriction of the afferent or efferent blood supply.

ISOTOPE FRACTIONATION

This technique depends upon the fact that if a foreign substance is given intravenously in a single dose, the substance will be distributed to the organs in proportion to their blood flow. The substance will then be carried away from the organs by their venous drainage. For a certain period of time, the venous drainage will be negligibly small compared to the arterial delivery, and during this time the fractional distribution of the substance among the organs will correspond to the fractional distribution of the cardiac output. The time in which venous drainage of the substance is small will depend upon the amount transferred from blood to tissue. Sapirstein (1956) has found that radioactive rubidium (Rb^{86}) has a very complete transfer to the tissues and he has used the technique extensively in rats to determine the distribution of the cardiac output. Following a single injection of Rb^{86}, the animals are killed and the radioactivity of individual organs determined. A possible ource of error is the presence of shunts (Sapirstein, 1958a). A major difficulty is that only one set of observations can be made on an individual animal.

MEASUREMENT OF VISCERAL BLOOD VOLUME

The method of measuring blood volume with the radioactive isotope P^{32} has been modified to measure the volume of a part of the splanchnic circulation. The arterial supply to the circulation in question is temporarily occluded and the isotope given intravenously. The blood volume measured is the total blood volume less the excluded circulation. When the excluded area is opened, the blood mixes with and dilutes the radioactive blood in the general circulation, giving a measure of the volume of the excluded section. This technique has been used in dogs by Delorme, MacPherson, Mukherjee and Rowlands (1951) and by Horvath, Kelly, Folk and Hutt (1957).

VISUAL OBSERVATION OF THE MICROCIRCULATION

The measurement of flow distribution on the macroscopic scale can be approached by cannulation of different vessels. The detailed behaviour of blood flow in smaller vessels can, however, only be approached by visual observation. One such approach to the study of the circulation in the mesentery of rat and dog was made by Chambers and Zweifach in 1944. Their methods have proved valuable in the study of the reactivity of vessels in relation to vasoactive nerves, drugs and hypotension. Microscopic studies must always be regarded as complementary to macroscopic studies since total flow in any tissue is a statistical integration of the flow through component units.

The technique of illumination of the intestine using quartz rods which permit the conduction of an intense light to the tissue with minimal heating effects has been used in rats by Oppenheimer and Mann (1943) and by Noer, Robb and Jacobsen (1951) in the rabbit.

Richens (1948) has used a combination of freeze drying and microscopy for the study of vasomotor activity in the rat intestine. A loop of duodenum is exposed, and after injection into the blood of the agent under study, the loop is quickly frozen at minus 70 to 78°C in a Dewar flask with dry ice and acetone. Sections are cut and examined under the microscope The technique offers an approach to the study of small vessels in the intestinal wall.

TECHNIQUES FOR THE STUDY OF GASTRO-INTESTINAL BLOOD
FLOW IN MAN

Although the assessment of gastro-intestinal blood flow in man presents many difficulties, human observations have also provided useful information.

The use of colour changes in bowel mucosa

The first recorded use of colour change as an index of blood flow responses was probably the classic case of traumatic gastrostomy (Alexis St. Martin) reported by Beaumont (1847). Beaumont was primarily interested in gastric secretion. Nevertheless he did report colour changes in relation to gastric function.

Attempts to determine the qualitative behaviour of the gastric circulation using the colour of gastric mucosa as the index of change really derive from the work of Wolf and Wolff (1943). They observed colour changes in the exposed mucosae of gastrostomies, mainly in children. Despite the simplicity of their approach they made many observations of fundamental importance. Observations on colour changes in the colon had been made earlier by White, Cobb and Jones (1939) (and on the exposed colonic mucosa of the dog by Drury, Florey and Florey, 1929). The observations of White, Cobb and Jones were less detailed than those of Wolf and Wolff. They used the sigmoidoscope to observe responses in the colons of normal students and investigated the colour reactions of the mucosa to various vasoactive drugs. Almy and Tulin (1947) observed colour reactions in the rectal mucosa of young adult males and applied their method to the study of "stress" (by which they meant mechanically induced headaches, cold or pain).

Temperature methods in bowel blood flow measurement

Shoskes (1948) attempted to measure surface temperature of colostomy tissue but failed to secure satisfactory apposition with thermopiles and he discarded the method, and resorted to the use of colour to investigate the local application of vasoactive drugs.

Grayson (1949) recorded temperature from the exposed bowel tissues of colostomies. He used fine-gauge needle thermocouples inserted into the mucosa, or in some cases the muscle, of the exposed gut. It was argued that colostomy temperature could be used as a qualitative index of blood flow, in the same way as skin temperature. Thus a rise in tissue temperature indicated an increase in blood flow; a fall in temperature, a fall in blood flow.

Many colostomy subjects had two abdominal stomata, one associated with the bowel proximal to the colostomy and the other associated with the bowel distal to the colostomy. In such cases, one stoma could be used for experimental observation while the other, infiltrated with novocaine, provided a denervated control—a useful method in investigating reflex responses.

Such methods have produced valuable results, but it should be borne in mind that the tissue of the colostomy is exposed to a temperature lower than the normal intraperitoneal temperature, that the patient has undergone an operation with possible damage to the colon or its nerve supply, and that newly acquired vascular communications with the surrounding skin might influence the results in some cases.

Measurements of rectal temperature

Attempts have been made to develop heat exchange methods for the determination of blood flow in the rectum of normal subjects.

Grayson (1951b) used an instrument consisting of a small sphere of copper carrying a heating filament and a thermocouple. The cold junction was enclosed in the polyethylene tube which carried the leads. The instrument was inserted into the rectum as far as the ampulla where it lay enveloped in folds of mucosa. It was considered that a rise in blood flow would produce a drop in the temperature of the heated sphere, a fall in flow would permit its temperature to rise. Bowel movements were recorded separately from a balloon and blood flow readings only taken during periods of quiescence (which, in the normal rectum—though not in the sympathectomized rectum—were usually long-lasting). The method was relatively insensitive and was purely qualitative; it was, however, responsive to large blood flow changes such as occurred in the experimental faint.

IV

THE CONTROL OF THE GASTRO-INTESTINAL CIRCULATION

The magnitude of gastro-intestinal flow

The first attempts to determine the magnitude of gastro-intestinal flow were made from measurements of total flow in the portal vein (Schmid, 1908; Burton-Opitz, 1911iv). Table 4.1 shows the values obtained by various techniques in the dog, cat and rat, and if a spleen blood flow of about 10 per cent of these values is allowed for (see Chapter X) the magnitude of gastro-intestinal flow can be assessed. When the average values for total blood flow found by Burton-Opitz (1911) determined with the stromuhr are compared on a body weight basis with those of Green *et al.* (1959) determined with an electromagnetic flowmeter, the values are 18·9 and 16·6 ml./min/kg respectively. The values obtained by Burton-Opitz seem acceptable today. Nevertheless it should be borne in mind that determinations with techniques which involve exclusion of individual blood supplies may affect the value of the flow being measured.

Direct measurement of flow in the superior mesenteric artery in the dog with the thermostromuhr and the electromagnetic flowmeter, with and without cannulation, have given widely different results. From the data supplied by Grodins, Osborne, Ivy and Goldman (1941), using the thermostromuhr in dogs with a weight range of 9–25 kg, the average value was 227 ml./min. Deal and Green (1956), using the electromagnetic flowmeter, gave an average value of only 32 ml./min for an estimated two-thirds of the intestine in dogs of average weight 18·5 kg. This value contrasts with Deal and Green's own data (Table 4.1) for total portal inflow. This may well be due to the fact that, whereas their portal inflow data were obtained using a non-cannulating technique, their mesenteric artery flows used a cannulating method with substantial operative interference. It may be doubted whether such methods are of any real value in the assessment of total mesenteric blood flow.

From data given by Gregg (1962) flows of about 400 ml./min were found in dogs of 23 kg when recorded by chronically implanted electromagnetic flow recorders.

TABLE 4.1

Values for total portal inflow

Reference	Animal	Wt/kg	Total flow ml./min	Method
Burton-Opitz (1911iv)	Dog	14·3	268	Stromuhr
Grab *et al.* (1929)	Dog	9·6	200	Thermostromuhr
Blalock & Mason (1936)	Dog	11·5–18·8	309	Direct collection
Grindlay *et al.* (1941)	Dog	16·7	206–473	Thermostromuhr
Grodins *et al.* (1941)	Dog	9–25	163	Thermostromuhr
Green *et al.* (1959)	Dog	20·7	343	Electromagnetic flowmeter
Schmid (1908)	Cat	3	21·6	Stromuhr
Barcroft & Shore (1912)	Cat	3	20	Direct collection
Sapirstein *et al.* (1960)	Rat	0·2	9·0	Isotope fractionation

Note: Value for Schmid (1908) calculated from a liver wt of 87 g (Barcroft & Shore, 1912).
Average values for animal weights and blood flow have been given where possible.

Distribution of blood flow

There is evidence that despite the apparent free availability of blood to all parts of the gastro-intestinal tract, the vascular distribution is by no means uniform. Burton-Opitz (1908*a*) found in the dog that outflow from the intestine was 31 ml./100 g/min, and from the stomach 21 ml./100 g/min (Burton-Opitz, 1910*a*). Steiner and Mueller (1961), using an isotope fractionation technique, investigated functional perfusion rates of alimentary tissues in the rat. Blood flow for 100 g of tissue/min was 40 ml. in the stomach, 110 ml. in the duodenum, 90 ml. in the jejunum, 70 ml. in the ileum, 50 ml. in the caecum and 60 ml. in the colon. Thus blood flow per unit mass of tissue was highest in the duodenum and gradually became less as the caecum was approached. Similar findings were reported by Geber (1960) in the dog using the electromagnetic flowmeter with cannulation. His values per 100 g tissue/min were: duodenum 139 ml., jejunum 98 ml., ileum 83 ml. and colon 73 ml. These values are appreciably higher than those found by Burton-Opitz (1910*a*) although his values for total portal flow agree quite well with his estimated flow made from calculation of average organ flows and average organ weights (Burton-Opitz, 1911iv).

There have been a number of assessments of intestinal volume as a percentage of total blood volume. Mall (1892) stimulated the splanchnic nerves of the dog and measured the amount of blood that was required to be withdrawn to prevent a rise in blood pressure. He gave values of 10-27 per cent of the total blood volume. Delorme *et al.* (1951), using an isotope dilution method in the dog, gave an average total blood volume of 1,455 ml., a splanchnic blood volume of 495 ml. and an average mesenteric blood volume of 278 ml. Horvath *et al.* (1957), using a similar technique in the dog, gave an average total blood volume of 1,307 ml., a total splanchnic volume of 280 ml. and a mesenteric blood volume of 116 ml. In man, the average splanchnic blood volume determined by an isotope dilution method (see Chapter VI), and which includes liver blood volume, has been estimated as 20 per cent of the total blood volume (Wade, Combes, Childs, Wheeler, Cournard and Bradley, 1956), confirming previous observations by Bradley, Inglefinger and Bradley (1952) and Bradley, Marks, Reynell and Meltzer (1953).

The effect of adrenaline and noradrenaline on bowel blood flow

Oliver and Schäfer (1895) suggested that the rise in blood pressure which followed the injection of an extract of the adrenal gland was due largely to the contraction of the arterioles of the splanchnic area. This view was agreed by Brodie and Dixon (1904). Hoskins and Gunning (1917), however, investigated the effects on intestinal volume and intestinal outflow of adrenaline in the dog and reported that either contraction or dilatation could occur. Clarke (1930) measured intestinal and limb volume in cats and rabbits. Adrenaline in an amount sufficient to raise the blood pressure caused a prolonged vasoconstriction in the skin and a dilatation in voluntary muscle and intestine after an initial constriction. The dilatation of intestine and muscle beds was partly reflex from the rise in blood pressure, but it was also seen after section of the vagus and splanchnic nerves. If the blood pressure rise was prevented, there was constriction in the intestine and muscle but more transient and less marked in the skin. The rise in portal pressure which occurred was not responsible for the intestinal vasodilatation. In a further investigation, Clarke (1934), measuring venous outflow from the intestine with a drop recorder, showed that the smallest effective amount of adrenaline always produced a diminution in blood flow from the intestine and the skin. In the intestine the response could be reversed by the administration of ergotoxine. He considered the dilator effect of adrenaline after ergotoxine to indicate the presence of vasodilator nerve endings in the sympathetic supply to the intestine. Bülbring and Burn (1936) examined the effects of adrenaline on the intestinal circulation of the dog and cat, using a plethysmograph. The vagi were cut and the suprarenal glands removed. In the dog, large doses of adrenaline were vasoconstrictor, the effect being reversed by ergotoxine. Small doses of adrenaline caused a small fall in blood pressure and vasodilatation. In the cat the results were similar but less marked.

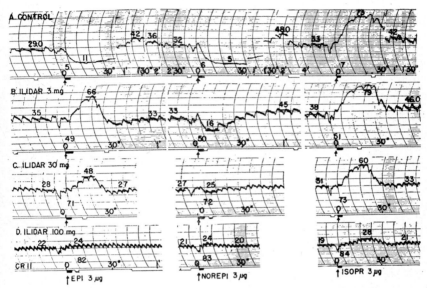

FIG. 4.1. Typical flow responses in mesenteric vascular bed of the dog to intra-arterial infusion of 3 μg each of 1-epinephrine (adrenaline) (EPI), 1-norepinephrine (noradrenaline) (NOREPI) and isopropylnorepinephrine (ISOPR).

A—Control; B—Ilidar, 3 mg; C—Ilidar, 30 mg; D—Ilidar, 100 mg. Figures gives the rate of flow ml./minute.

(From Green, Deal, Barhanabaedya and Denison, 1955.)

When the intestinal blood flow was measured by collection of the intestinal outflow, the dilator effect of adrenaline was more difficult to elicit.

These findings were largely substantiated by Green, Deal, Bardhanabaedya and Denison (1955), who showed, from measurements of superior mesenteric artery flow with an electromagnetic flowmeter in the dog, that adrenaline and noradrenaline were vaso constrictor, that isopropylnoradrenaline was vasodilator, and that following adrenergic blockade with ilidar (azapetine phosphate),

adrenaline and isopropylnoradrenaline produced vasodilator effects
(Fig. 4.1). Noradrenaline did not produce vasodilatation after
ilidar.

These results can be explained in terms of the receptor theory
of Ahlquist (1948). Ergotoxine and ilidar block α receptors and
the presence of vasodilatation after the administration of these
substances, or with isopropylnoradrenaline, implies the presence
of β receptors (Fig. 2.5).

The action of adrenaline and noradrenaline has been demonstrated to be predominantly vasoconstrictor in the mesentery of the
cat (Chambers and Zweifach, 1944), in the human bowel wall by
Friedman and Snape (1946) and by Shoskes (1948), who used the
colour of exposed mucosa of colostomies as an index of vascular
reaction. The local application of adrenaline produced marked
blanching. A similar observation had previously been reported on
the exposed colonic mucosa of the dog (Drury, Florey and Florey,
1929).

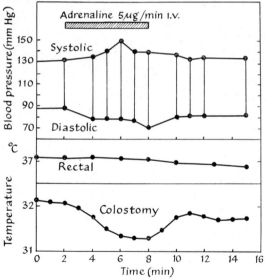

FIG. 4.2. The effect of intravenous infusions of adrenaline on rectal
temperature, blood pressure and colostomy temperature in man.
(Grayson and Swan, 1950*a*.)

Clear evidence of sympathomimetic vasoconstriction in man was
also obtained by Grayson and Swan (1950*a*) using subjects on
whom colostomy had been performed. Fig. 4.2 shows the results

of an intravenous infusion of adrenaline. There was a marked drop in bowel temperature with a rise in mean systemic blood pressure. Similar results were obtained both in colon and ileum and must be considered clear evidence of vasoconstriction.

The effect of acetylcholine on bowel blood flow

The action of acetylcholine on bowel blood flow is controversial. Necheles, Frank, Kaye and Rosenman (1936) perfused the isolated stomach of the rat with Locke's solution at room temperature (because the preparation was more stable). They found a reduction of flow of about 17 per cent in 44 out of 45 perfusions with acetylcholine. Perfusion of limb vessels under the same conditions always produced vasodilatation. Gut motility was not recorded but they mention that motility was affected by acetylcholine under these conditions only occasionally. Necheles, Levitsky, Kohn, Maskin and Frank (1936) carried out similar experiments in the dog with both denervated and innervated stomachs, the latter being performed *in situ*. In 17 experiments a small dose of acetylcholine (0·01–1·0 µg/min) caused a decrease in blood flow of 30 per cent. Larger doses of acetylcholine (5–40 µg/min) increased flow by 30 per cent. In three experiments there was only a diminution in flow, and in seven experiments only an increase in flow. They considered the effects of contraction of the bowel, which was present in this preparation, but made no simultaneous measurement.

Bülbring and Burn (1936) found that in the dog intestine, small doses of acetylcholine caused a fall in intestinal volume and blood pressure. In the cat, acetylcholine sometimes caused an increase in intestinal volume but often showed similar responses to the dog. Gotsev (1940) analysed the action of acetylcholine in more detail. He was able to show local dilatation with close arterial injection in the dog. Systemic infusions, however, which lowered the blood pressure were usually accompanied by a reduced bowel blood flow, partly mechanical, partly reflex. Walder (1952) perfused fifteen isolated human stomachs with plasma containing 1 mg/100 ml. eserine and 10 µg/ml. of acetylcholine. Vasoconstriction occurred in eight perfusions and vasodilatation in seven.

It will be seen later that intestinal tone and motility can profoundly affect bowel blood flow. There have been no studies in which the effect of acetylcholine has been studied in relation to these factors. It seems likely that acetylcholine is dilator to blood

vessels in the gastro-intestinal tract but that the effects may be
obscured by an increase in tone of the bowel wall.

THE AUTONOMIC NERVOUS SYSTEM AND BOWEL BLOOD FLOW

Sympathetic stimulation

There is little doubt that the predominant effect of splanchnic
nerve stimulation is vasoconstriction of the intestinal vessels. Mall
(1892) used splanchnic nerve stimulation to produce a rise in blood
pressure; Bayliss and Starling (1899) noticed that the intestine
became paler, and Bunch (1899) recorded a reduction in intestinal
volume. Burton-Opitz (1910b) recorded a reduction in outflow
from an intestinal vein and a reduction in total portal flow from
240 ml./min to 60 ml./min (Burton-Opitz, 1912). Bradford (1889)
found, however, that in the dog a fall in blood pressure could be
produced if the splanchnic nerves were stimulated with stimuli at
low frequencies (1 per sec). He interpreted this as due to the existence of vasodilator fibres to the bowel passing in the splanchnic
nerve. Bunch (1899) similarly reported that weak stimuli resulted
in bowel vasodilatation in the dog. This effect did not appear to be
due to incidental stimulation of vagal fibres, for although Latschenberger and Deahna (1876) and Hallion and Francois-Franck (1896)
had previously reported that vagal stimulation cause dilatation of
gut vessels, this could not be confirmed by Bayliss and Starling
(1899) in the dog or by Bunch (1899) in the dog, cat or rabbit.
Bayliss (1923) considered that there was no evidence for dilator
fibres supplying the gut of the cat or rabbit.

Bülbring and Burn (1936) stimulated the splanchnic nerves in
the dog and cat after excluding the adrenal circulation. Splanchnic
stimulation resulted in a reduction of gut volume, but after ergotoxine, stimulation regularly produced an increase in gut volume
(Fig. 4.3). The response was not affected by eserine and could not
be abolished by atropine, and was not therefore cholinergic in
origin. The response was similar but less clear in the cat. Bülbring
and Burn did not consider it necessary to postulate the presence of
vasodilator fibres in the splanchnics and suggested that the result
could be related to the action of adrenaline on blood vessels.
Folkow, Frost and Uvnäs (1948) measured portal outflow in the
cat. The adrenal glands were removed. Splanchnic nerve stimulation after blockade with dibenamine (10 mg/kg) resulted in a slight
increase in flow. Deal and Green (1956), using electromagnetic

flowmeters in the dog, found that the constrictor response to splanchnic nerve stimulation could be abolished by adrenergic blockade with ilidar, but with large blocking doses of this drug there was a primary dilator response which was not abolished by atropine.

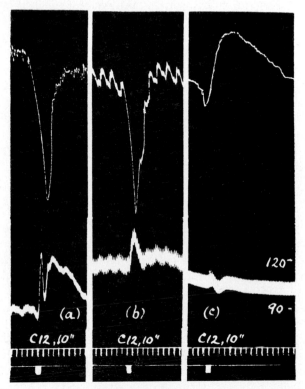

FIG. 4.3. Dog. The effect of splanchnic stimulation on the volume of an intestinal loop. Suprarenals removed.

(*a*) Stimulation—causing reduction in gut volume.
(*b*) Intravenous adrenaline—reduction in gut volume.
(*c*) Ergotoxine injection—increase in gut volume.

(From Bülbring and Burn, 1936.)

Lindgren and Uvnäs (1953) measured venous outflow from the mesenteric vessels of the dog and cat, and were able to define a medullary area of the brain which on stimulation produced clear evidence of intestinal vasoconstriction while at the same time vaso-dilatation was recorded in skeletal muscle which could be blocked by atropine. They were not able to define any medullary area of the brain which on stimulation would produce intestinal vaso-dilatation.

It is clear from the effects of atropine that there are no cholin-ergic fibres supplying the blood vessels of the bowel. The vaso-dilatation which occurs when the sympathetic nerve is stimulated after ergotoxine or ilidar probably cannot be explained in terms of β receptor stimulation by locally released adrenaline. In the experiments of Deal and Green it is possible that the vasodilatation they reported may have been due to circulating adrenaline released from the adrenal gland during splanchnic stimulation. This could not have been the case in the experiments of Bülbring and Burn since they were performed after adrenalectomy. Folkow, Frost and Uvnäs (1948) suggested that, since even large doses of blocking agent did not prevent the inhibitory effect of sympathetic stimula-tion on bowel tone, the rise in blood flow found by them could have been due to reduction of extravascular compression.

Sympathetic section

There is evidence that the sympathetic supply to the bowel is tonically active. Bayliss and Starling (1899) noted that the bowel of the dog became red after splanchnic nerve section. Izquierdo and Koch (1930) observed a fall in blood pressure in the rabbit of 30 per cent and Kremer and Wright (1932) found, using a plethys-mograph, evident vasodilatation in the splanchnic area of the cat after splanchnic nerve section. Richens (1948), using a rapid freez-ing technique combined with microscopy of the bowel wall, found that in the rat, ergotoxine caused a dilatation of arteries, arterioles and veins of the duodenum. The existence of autonomically medi-ated vascular tone in human bowel has been shown by Grayson (1950), using subjects on whom the operation of colostomy had been performed. Temperatures were recorded from the exposed tissue using fine-gauge needle thermocouples. Fig. 4.4. shows the results of a number of observations on different subjects in which the temperature was recorded before and after infiltrating the bowel with "procaine". In each case this procedure resulted in a rise in bowel temperature. The evidence suggests the existence of vaso-motor tone but does not prove it to be sympathetic. In favour of a sympathetic mediation is the fact that adrenaline or noradrenaline produced marked vasoconstriction in the bowel (Grayson and Swan, 1950a) and that atropine infiltration of the colostomy had no effect.

The autonomic control of vascular tone in the bowel of the human seems to be unstable. Wolf and Wolff (1943) from observations on gastric mucosa, and Almy and Tulin (1947) from observations on gastrostomies and colostomies, reported colour changes

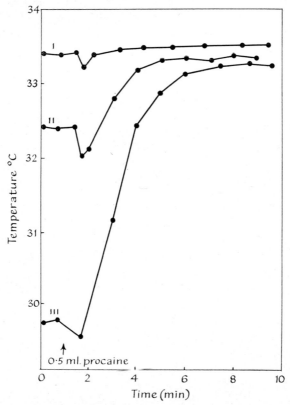

FIG. 4.4. The effect of local infiltration of procaine hydrochloride on the temperature of colostomy tissue (man) exposed to room air at constant temperature. Three subjects. Temperature rise in subjects II and III accompanied by visible flushing of the bowel.

(Grayson, 1950.)

in the mucosa which occurred sometimes at random and sometimes in relation to specific stimuli. Thus, in children emotional stimuli such as fright or anger would frequently produce flushing of the bowel without concomitant change in systemic blood pressure, indicating, so they claimed, increase in blood flow due to alterations of autonomic activity. It is interesting to note that Drury, Florey and Florey (1929) had shown that the exposed colonic mucosa of the dog would blanch after minor stimuli (sudden noise) for about 10–15 seconds.

The extent of capillary filtration in the intestine of the cat, and its relation to blood flow, has been examined by Folkow *et al.* (1963). The volume of a denervated loop of jejunum was recorded from a preparation in which arterial inflow pressure was controlled by graded aortic constriction. Venous outflow was measured with a drop recorder. The rate of capillary filtration was determined by the method of Mellander (1960). Venous outflow pressure was first adjusted so that there was no change in the volume of the loop, implying that outward and inward filtration at the capillary level were equal. The venous outflow pressure was then increased by a few mm Hg. The volume of the loop increased rapidly due to distension of the venous bed, and then more slowly due to the outward filtration caused by a raised capillary hydrostatic pressure. From this "filtration slope" the rate of capillary filtration could be determined.

In the acutely denervated intestine, the range of blood flow was 40–60 ml./min/100 g intestine, and the capillary filtration coefficient 0·17 ml./min/100 g/mm Hg. Flow increases of up to 270 ml./min/100 g were obtained with large doses of isopropylnoradrenaline given intra-arterially, and at this flow level, the capillary filtration coefficient was of the order of 0·4 ml./min/100 g/mm Hg. These values are ten times those reported for skeletal muscle by Cobbold *et al.* (1963). On the assumption that the maximum blood flow capacity and capillary filtration coefficient of the smooth muscle of the intestine would not exceed that of skeletal muscle, Folkow *et al.* (1963) postulated that maximal blood flow in the mucosal portion of the intestine was more likely to be of the order of 500 ml./min/100 g tissue, and that capillary filtration capacity is of a similar magnitude to filtration in the renal glomeruli. Such an arrangement would be ideal for the secretory and absorptive functions of the intestine, but a small change in capillary pressure could lead to marked oedema, unless some protective mechanism were brought into play.

The existence of such a mechanism has been shown by Folkow *et al.* (1964), using a similar preparation to that described above. When the sympathetic fibres to the loop of jejunum were stimulated at rates of from 2–8 impulses/sec there was a decrease in venous outflow lasting 30–40 sec, which in some cases suggested that "critical closure" had occurred. Although stimulation was continued, blood flow gradually recovered until in the steady state resistance was some 20–30 per cent above that of the control period. Recovery of blood flow, "autoregulatory escape" was more complete with the fastest rates of stimulation. During the period of autoregulatory escape, there was no change in gut volume which was interpreted as indicating a constant precapillary to postcapillary resistance ratio and a constant capillary filtration. Folkow *et al.* (1964*a*) suggested that the autoregulatory escape occurred somewhere within the "precapillary resistance section" and that the phenomenon was important for the protection of mean capillary pressure.

It was noted by Folkow *et al.* (1964*a*) that following the cessation of nerve stimulation, reactive hyperaemia regularly occurred, although the blood flow during the period of "autoregulatory escape" had not been markedly reduced. This suggested that there may have been a redistribution of blood in the intestine so that some areas were in a state of ischaemia while others were overperfused. That this was so has been shown by Folkow *et al.* (1964*b*). Frozen microtome sections of the gut obtained after the intra-arterial injection of India ink during the various phases of nerve stimulation showed a severe reduction of mucosal vessel filling during the period of flow restriction, with only a limited recovery during the period of autoregulatory escape. Less marked reductions of filling with India ink occurred in the muscularis and serosa. It was evident that during sympathetic nerve stimulation blood had been directed from the mucosa possibly to submucosal shunt vessels.

THE CONTROL OF ARTERIO-VENOUS ANASTOMOSES IN THE BOWEL

The discovery of arterio-venous anastomoses in the skin aroused speculation as to their function. Grant and Bland (1931), who studied them in human skin, and Clark and Clark (1934) from observations on the rabbit ear, regarded their function as specifically related to temperature regulation. Clara (1937) took a wider view of arterio-venous anastomoses and implicated them in peripheral resistance adjustments to blood pressure regulation.

The control of arterio-venous anastomoses in the human stomach has been examined by Walder (1952). He perfused fresh human stomachs, obtained at operation, with a perfusate containing glass spheres of known diameters. The conditions of the experiments were varied in relation to perfusion pressure, temperature, oxygenation, pH, nerve stimulation and drugs. The venous outflow was collected and the number and sizes of spheres obtained was determined.

The existence of arterio-venous anastomoses was confirmed by his finding that spheres of up to 140 μ could be collected in the outflow fluid, a size too large to pass through a capillary bed, and indicating that the maximum diameter of the arterio-venous anastomoses was of this order. A second important point was that the same size distribution of spheres was found in the outflow whatever the experimental conditions, which suggested that the arterio-venous anastomoses were either fully open or completely shut, but did not maintain intermediate positions, an observation which fits well with the suppositions of Burton (1951). Alternatively, the anastomoses may have been constantly open, a varied proportion of the total flow taking place through them.

The essential findings in Walder's experiments are shown in Table 4.2. In general, an increase in the number of spheres

TABLE 4.2

Factors affecting perfusion rate and passage of glass spheres through the vessels of the human stomach *in vitro*. (After Walder, 1952.)

Experiment	Total perfusion rate	Concentration of glass spheres/ml. in venous outflow
Perfusion pressure raised	increased	no change
Temperature lowered	decreased	increased
Oxygen saturation		
(a) low	(a) increased	(a) no change
(b) high	(b) decreased	(b) no change
pH raised from 7·4 to 7·6	decreased	decreased
Nerve stimulation	decreased	increased
Adrenaline	decreased	increased
Acetylcholine	(a) decreased	(a) increased
(either (a) or (b))	(b) increased	(b) decreased in 2 out of 6 experiments to zero
Histamine	increased	decreased

recovered in the perfusate occurred when the perfusion rate decreased. The inference drawn by Walder is that capillary hindrance to flow is the main determinant of the amount of fluid passing through the arterio-venous anastomoses. Changes in pH were unusual in that when the pH was 7·6, there was both reduced flow and a reduction in the number of spheres recovered, the conclusion being that closure of anastomoses had occurred. It is of interest to note that change in perfusion pressure did not alter the number of spheres in the outflow.

In the remainder of the gastro-intestinal tract arterio-venous anastomoses have been harder to demonstrate than in the stomach. Grim and Lindseth (1958) have studied the proportion of flow passing through arterio-venous anastomoses in dog intestine *in situ*, by means of glass spheres of known diameter labelled with radioactive sodium (Na^{24}). Spheres of known size were injected into a mesenteric artery, venous blood was collected for 2 minutes, the gut was then removed and the radioactivity of the mucosa, submucosa, muscle and mesentery determined. With spheres of 43 μ in diameter only 1 per cent of the injected radioactive material was found in the venous outflow. This, they considered, was probably radioactive sodium washed out of the spheres and they consider that all the arterio-venous channels were less than 43 μ in diameter. This is a figure very much less than that reported by Walder for the stomach and, failing satisfactory histological demonstration of their anatomy, the true nature of arterio-venous anastomoses in the gastro-intestinal tract must remain speculative.

The role, too, of such channels where they exist is doubtful, but it would seem possible that they follow passively changes in mucosal circulation and offer an alternative route for blood flow whenever the mucosal vessels are constricted. It seems unlikely from the data produced by Walder that they are under autonomic nervous control.

THE CONTROL OF MESENTERIC VEINS

The importance of the splanchnic venous bed as a potential site for the storage of blood has been investigated by Alexander, Edwards and Ankency (1953). Pressure/volume diagrams were constructed for the venous bed of ileal loops in the dog. The arterial supply and venous outflow of the loop were temporarily occluded, and the pressure within the venous bed determined after injection of a known volume of blood into it. The response is shown in Fig. 4.5. Immediately following the injection of blood there was a rapid rise in pressure, which gradually declined. According to Alexander *et al.*, the rapid rise in pressure is due to the limited distensibility of the venous bed due to the elastic tissue in the walls of veins. The fall in pressure with time is attributed to "delayed compliance" or passive yielding of the walls which is related to the visco-elastic property of smooth muscle. It would seem that transient elevations of portal pressure would not cause significant pooling of blood because of the elastic component of the venous bed, but pooling would be favoured by maintained elevation of portal

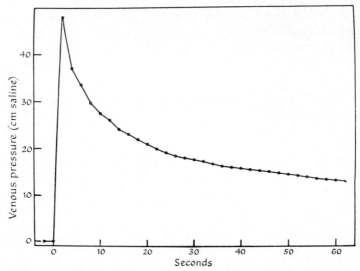

FIG. 4.5. Dog. Changes in mesenteric venous pressure following rapid injection of 3 ml. blood into the vein of an intestinal loop. Arterial inflow and venous outflow occluded; all collateral vessels ligated.

(From Alexander, Edwards and Ankeney, 1953.)

pressure. The effect of adrenaline and noradrenaline on the distensibility of the venous splanchnic bed was investigated by Alexander (1954a). The results obtained depended upon the pressures within the veins. When the pressure within the venous bed was normal, adrenergic stimulation increased the distensibility of the splanchnic venous system, that is to say, the venous system could contain more blood for the same change in pressure. When the venous pressure was low, adrenaline decreased the distensibility. The explanation offered by Alexander is that the muscular component of the vein wall is more distensible than other elements. When the muscle is contracted with adrenaline, it carries more of the load, which is reflected by the increased distensibility. When the pressure is low there is a tendency for the vessels to close with a resultant decrease in distensibility. The importance of these results is that adrenergic stimulation of the splanchnic venous system when the venous pressure is low, might be expected to constrict the veins and mobilize blood for the systemic circulation. On the other hand, if the splanchnic venous pressure were normal, adrenergic stimulation might be expected to increase the distensibility of the system and promote pooling of blood with minimal changes in pressure.

There is a relationship between portal pressure and resistance to gastro-intestinal inflow. Selkurt and Johnson (1958) measured portal vein pressures and flow (by rotameter) in the dog; they used bowel weight as an indication of arterial inflow. When portal pressure was increased by obstruction to the outflow the resistance of the mesenteric bed increased proportionately. Thus a two-fold increase in portal pressure caused a 30 per cent reduction in arterial inflow, and a three-fold increase in pressure a 44 per cent reduction of inflow. The response did not appear to be due to tissue fluid accumulation and persisted after denervation of the arterial supply.

The phenomenon has been examined further by Johnson (1959), who confirmed that the response persisted after painting the arterial wall with procaine, but was attenuated by papaverine, which is an arterial relaxant, by cyanide and by ischaemia. The rise in pressure in the venous system is transmitted to the artery and Johnson considers the response is myogenic, that is, a feature of the smooth muscle in the artery. Alexander (1956) has shown that the calibre of the mesenteric veins may be reflexly adjusted in response to an elevation of pressure in the abdominal caval system. When a balloon was inflated in the inferior vena cava of the dog near the right heart, or a rise in venous pressure induced with an artificial mitral stenosis, dilatation occurred in the veins of the intestine. The phenomenon was reflex, for it could be abolished by vagotomy. The efferent limb was the sympathetic supply. The responses were not mechanical, because the intestinal loop under study was isolated apart from its nervous connections.

Baroreceptors and the splanchnic circulation

It is clear that baroreceptor activity in the aortic arch and carotid sinus can affect intestinal blood flow, and it is possible that there are splanchnic baroreceptors which can affect systemic blood pressure.

Bayliss (1893) showed that stimulation of the central end of the depressor nerve in the dog resulted in vasodilatation in the intestine.

Similar observations have been made by Jarisch and Ludwig (1926), by Tournade (1930), who found that stimulation of the sinus nerve was equally effective, and by Heymans, Bouckaert and Dautrelbe (1930), who reported vasodilatation in the intestine on raising the pressure in the carotid sinus. Koch and Nordmann (1928) also found intestinal vasoconstriction on occluding the carotid artery—and thereby, they assumed, lowering the sinus pressure.

The relative importance of the intestinal circulation in the baro-receptor reflex was indicated by Izquierdo and Koch (1930), who found that splanchnic nerve section in the rabbit caused a 30 per cent drop in blood pressure if the aortic and sinus nerves were intact, but a 70 per cent drop in blood pressure if these nerves had been previously sectioned. The problem was investigated in more detail by Kremer and Wright (1932) in the cat. Splanchnic nerve section caused a drop in blood pressure of 0–15 per cent, with evident dilatation in the splanchnic area as determined by plethys-mography. When the buffer nerves were inactivated first, splanchnic nerve section caused a drop in pressure of 50 per cent. The rise in blood pressure from occlusion of the carotids was also diminished as a result of splanchnic nerve section. The interesting feature was that fairly complete compensation of blood pressure after splanchnic nerve section could still occur and Kremer and Wright suggested that skeletal muscle was probably the area where compensation occurred.

Alexander (1954*b*) has shown that the mesenteric veins are also involved in baroreceptor reflexes. Decrease in carotid sinus pres-sure decreased the distensibility of mesenteric veins, which was interpreted as venoconstriction, and carotid sinus hypertension increased the distensibility of the venous bed, which was inter-preted as venodilatation. It would seem that in these circumstances the gastro-intestinal tract can be a labile blood store in addition to a variable peripheral resistance.

The significance of these findings in relation to the role of the splanchnic area as a whole in blood pressure regulation will be further considered in a later chapter.

Mesenteric baroreceptors

The importance of the mesenteric circulation as a site of baro-receptor activity is controversial. Gammon and Bronk (1935) claimed to have monitored afferent impulses which were initiated by vascular distension, from the peripheral ends of splanchnic nerves in the cat. They considered that the impulses came from Paccinian corpuscles in the mesentry, in close relation to the mesenteric vessels but with their own blood supply. Perfusion of the mesenteric bed at high pressure increased the impulse activity, decrease in pressure decreased the activity. Sarnoff and Yamada (1959) considered that the mesenteric area of the cat was a site of dominant baroreceptor activity. When the main vessels around the coeliac axis were temporarily occluded, systemic hypertension developed, and if the vessels in this area were perfused at high pressure, there was systemic hypotension. The responses were abolished by ganglion blockade. Bayer and Scher (1960) could not confirm Sarnoff and Yamad's finding for the cat or dog. They considered that a mechanical redistribution of blood accounted for previous findings. Heymans, De Schaepdryver and De Vleeschhouwer (1960) could not find evidence of mesenteric baroreceptor activity in the dog. Selkurt and Roth (1960) agreed with Sarnoff and Yamada for the cat and found that in the dog the sino-aortic reflexes hold the splanchnic mechanism in check, the responses being significantly increased if these areas were denervated.

The evidence does not allow firm conclusion to be drawn because it is impossible to denervate mesenteric baroreceptors without at the same time seriously altering the peripheral resistance of the intestine. It would, in any case, seem strange for a baroreceptor mechanism to be controlled by a section of the circulation which, itself, is generally considered a major site of the adjustable peripheral resistance.

LOCAL FACTORS AFFECTING GASTRO-INTESTINAL BLOOD FLOW

There is little information concerning vascular reactions in the gut in relation to its secretory or absorptive activities. According to Radostina (1953) there is in the pig mesentery, near the jejunum, a vascular "torus" of anastomosing arterial and venous vessels, which supply and drain the duodenum. Both the artery and vein of the torus are said to contain contractile elements which can cause closure of the vessels. During digestion, the torus supplies the jejunum with blood, and during quiescence the blood flows through the arterio-venous anastomoses of the torus thereby bypassing the jejunum. The mechanism is said to account for the high oxygen content of the portal vein during inactivity since the gut is by-passed; it also accounts for a high pressure in the portal vein—again because of the arterio-venous anastomoses.

There would seem to be no evidence for a similar anatomical provision in other species. This does not, however, preclude a similar function for arterio-venous anastomoses in the gastro-intestinal tract.

In conscious man, the portal venous oxygen content has been studied by Smythe, Fitzpatrick and Blakemore (1951), and whilst it is true that portal oxygen content may drop by 2 per cent during digestion, there is no evidence that portal venous pressure is also lowered under these conditions.

The effect of feeding on the distribution of blood in the bowel has been investigated by Grim and Lindseth (1958) in the dog using glass spheres labelled with radioactive sodium. Total flow was elevated by 31 per cent after feeding and the proportion of blood flowing through arterio-venous channels of 12 to 20 μ in diameter was doubled. Flow through larger anastomotic channels was unchanged. Capillary flow only increased in the muscle of the bowel and not in the mucosa.

Evidence relating to local vascular changes may seem to be scanty. The use of glass sphere perfusion in the assessment of a continuing and delicate physiological process must be viewed with caution. Most of the evidence which does not depend on the use of glass spheres suggests that digestive activity favours increased mucosal flow with less flow through anastomotic channels.

GASTRO-INTESTINAL VASCULAR RESPONSES TO INTRAENTERIC PRESSURE

One of the earliest discussions of this issue came from Mall (1896), who, on the basis of conjectural rather than experimental evidence, suggested that any rise in tension in the bowel, be it as a result of distention within or of increased muscular activity, might be expected to cause a diminution in bowel blood flow. He further concluded that passive rises in intraenteric pressure might be expected to have less effect than increased muscular activity.

Anrep, Cerqua and Samaan (1934) adduced more positive evidence to show that increased activity of the intestinal musculature reduced blood flow.

Lawson and Chumley (1940), using isolated loops of dog ileum, were, however, probably the first to obtain experimental evidence in this matter. Their experiments seemed to show that increasing the pressure in the lumen of the bowel up to 30 mm Hg had little or no effect on blood flow; raising the intraenteric pressure by pressures up to the mean mesenteric arterial pressure only had a transient effect in reducing flow, a considerable measure of recovery occurring even though the pressure were maintained. They took their observations further, simulating raised intramural tension by stretching a segment of the gut wall, and showed that this had a greater effect in reducing flow but that even with raised intramural pressure there was some recovery during the period of pressure. They produced evidence suggesting the existence of a local vaso-dilator reflex produced by stretching the wall of the intestine and mediated through local nervous mechanisms, its effect being to compensate for the added resistance to flow.

On the other hand, Oppenheimer and Mann (1943), using rats, and Noer, Robb and Jacobsen (1951), using rabbits, have shown by a quartz rod illumination technique that with intraluminal pressures of 15–20 mm Hg, segmental contractions in the intestines cease and that there is a slowing of blood in the serosal vessels. As the intraluminal pressure increases, the circulation ceases first on the venous side and then on the arterial side.

The reasons for the discrepancies arising from the observations of Lawson and Chumley are not clear. Nevertheless the weight of evidence supports the view that an increase in intraluminal pressure causes a reduction in flow in the intestinal wall.

THE EFFECT OF TONUS AND MOTILITY

The effect of tonus and motility on intestinal blood flow has been investigated by Sidky and Bean (1958), using the perfused isolated dog intestine. It was evident that the presence of rhythmic contractions had a "pumping" action on intestinal blood flow. During a contraction, arterial inflow was reduced and venous outflow increased, and the reverse occurred when the gut relaxed. Moreover, when tonus in the gut was high a reduced flow was found, which could obscure the effects of rhythmic contractions. Decreased tonus could allow a high flow even without contractions. These authors conclude that "intestinal tonus is an important determinant of functional blood reservoir capacity" and that peristalsis is an important factor in the propulsion of blood through the intestine.

THE EFFECT OF BLOOD OXYGEN SATURATION

There is evidence that anoxia may dilate vessels by a direct action and constrict them by sympathetic activity produced by anoxia. The problem is further complicated by the effect of anoxia on bowel tonus and motility and by the passive effects of a rise in

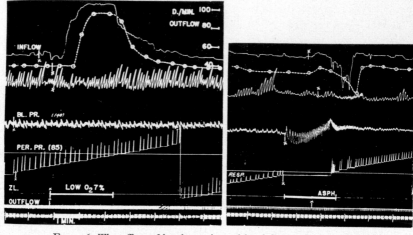

FIG. 4.6. The effect of local anoxia on blood flow in isolated, inner-vated segment of dog intestine. Animal breathing room air. From above downwards: inflow, plotted curve of outflow, intestinal contractions, blood pressure; constant perfusion pressure (Per. Pr.). Spirometer recording. ZL—zero line of blood pressure and perfusion pressure.

(Bean and Sidky, 1957.)

FIG. 4.7. Decrease in blood flow in isolated innervated segment of dog intestine with asphyxia (Asph.) Tracings as for Fig. 4.6.

(Bean and Sidky, 1957.)

blood pressure on the bowel vasculature. Bunch (1899) noted that with asphyxia in the dog, the intestinal vessels may dilate with the rise in blood pressure. Bernthal and Schwind (1945) measured changes in blood flow in the intestine and limb muscles of the dog, elicited reflexly by perfusion of anoxaemic blood (1 per cent oxygen) through the carotid body. The intestinal vessels were moderately reflexly constricted during carotid body anoxia and gradually returned to control conditions of flow, whereas the limb vessels showed a post-hypoxic dilatation, which they attributed to temporary inactivity of the vasomotor centre. The failure to elicit post-hypoxic dilatation in the intestinal vessels was attributed to vascular reflexes arising from Paccinian corpuscles of the mesentery (Gammon and Bronk, 1935).

Bean and Sidky (1957) have examined the effect of anoxia on intestinal blood flow and motility in perfused segments of dog gut, with and without an intact nerve supply. In both preparations, there was marked increase in intestinal blood flow when perfused with blood containing 7 per cent oxygen (Fig. 4.6). Intestinal motility was not affected. When the whole animal was made anoxic there was a decreased flow in the perfused intestine, and intestinal movement was inhibited (Fig. 4.7).

It would seem that the local effect of anoxia is vasodilator. In generalized anoxia or the even more extreme stimulus of asphyxia, other factors—one of them being sympathetic activity—overshadow the local action. A further factor under these circumstances may be the inhibition of bowel movement which, since bowel activity has been shown to enhance blood flow, might itself favour a diminution in blood flow to the bowel wall.

Alexander (1954) has shown that in the dog intestine, there is venoconstriction, as determined by distensibility curves with anoxia and hypercapnia, even though the blood pressure rose and might be expected to produce venodilatation by a baroreceptor reflex.

THE EFFECT OF LOCAL CHANGES IN TEMPERATURE

There is evidence that local cooling of the stomach wall results in vasoconstriction, and local warming in vasodilatation. Cutting, Dodds, Noble and Williams (1937) measured venous outflow from the stomach of the cat. The temperature was varied by circulating water through a rubber bag placed in the stomach. Cold water at 12°C caused a reduction in venous outflow from 16 ml./min to 7·0 ml./min, and hot water at 38–54°C a variable increase in venous outflow. Similar results were found by Salmon, Griffen and Wangensteen (1959) for the dog. Circulation of cold water at 15°C resulted in a mean fall in venous outflow of 68 per cent, and circulation of hot water at 48°C, a mean increase of venous outflow of 29 per cent. Wolf and Wolff (1943) found from observations of patients with a gastrostomy that local warming increased the redness of the mucosa, and local cooling caused blanching.

THE EFFECT OF EXTERNAL TEMPERATURE

It has been shown by Bisgard and Nye (1940) that motor activity in the bowel is inhibited by application of heat to the abdominal wall, and conversely is stimulated by application of cold.

The relation between environmental temperature and bowel blood flow was investigated by Grayson (1951*a*) in patients on whom colostomy had been performed. Temperatures from the colostomy and abdominal wall were recorded. When the legs were placed in hot water, the temperature of the colostomy fell, while the temperature of the abdominal skin remained relatively unchanged (Fig. 4.8). Similar responses could be elicited by warming

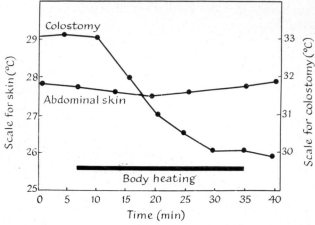

FIG. 4.8. Simultaneous recording from colostomy and skin of abdominal wall near the colostomy, showing vasoconstriction produced in the colon by body heating, with no corresponding change in the skin.

(Grayson, 1951*b*.)

limbs to which the circulation had been occluded. The fall in temperature of the colostomy could be abolished by infiltration with novocaine and thus appeared to be nervously mediated. Opposite changes were observed on placing the legs in cold water. These effects were regarded as part of a generalized adjustment of the peripheral resistance such as to compensate changes in skin blood flow. They were nervously mediated and may have been the result of baroreceptor activity, the effect of which was a redistribution of peripheral blood.

On the other hand, body heating of an intensity sufficient to raise the rectal temperature by 1 °C or more always produced a rise in colostomy temperature, which was greater than could be accounted for by the alteration in blood temperature and was accompanied by visible flushing of the colostomy. The reflex response to surface cold or warmth could not be elicited when the rectal temperature was thus raised. There was no final explanation for this observation. Grayson, however, regarded it as similar to the inhibition of vasomotor activity which an elevated "core" temperature has been shown to produce in the skin (Grayson, 1951*c*; Johnson, 1964) and skeletal muscle (Grayson, 1949*b*). If this be so this may be regarded merely as further evidence for the existence of tonic vasomotor activity in the bowel.

V

ANATOMY OF THE HEPATIC CIRCULATION

ANY study of the liver must logically begin with a consideration of its anatomy. Fortunately the subject has already been dealt with most adequately by a number of authors. Child (1954), for example, in his monograph gives an admirable survey of the development and detailed anatomy of this organ so that it is only necessary in the present work to outline the main points.

There has long been a tendency to consider the liver as a composite organ consisting of many separate and individually functioning units (Kiernan, 1833). The hepatic lobule is commonly regarded as a sort of tubular gland consisting of long columns of cells between which are channels filled with blood. Each lobule is thus, in itself, a sort of little liver, anatomically separate and functionally autonomous. Not everyone has lightly accepted this concept. Arey (1932), still thinking, however, in terms of "functioning units", arrived at the conclusion that the real physiological unit of the liver was a composite structure composed primarily of the peripheral parts of several lobules.

The idea of the liver as a composite of separate lobules lost considerable ground with the work of Kretz (1894), who elaborated the view of the liver as a structure which was essentially vascular, in which the framework was the hepatic venous tree. Its branches were a skeleton clothed in liver parenchyma. If this be a true picture it follows that there are no separate lobules and that these structures which stand out so vividly in section are merely that part of the liver tissue which envelops a particular radicle of the portal vein.

In all these descriptions of liver structure there was lacking the sound anatomical evidence on which alone a real picture of the organ might be built up. This deficiency, fortunately, has been largely remedied by the beautiful stereographic reconstructions of Elias (1949a & b), from the livers of humans, horses, dogs, cats, rabbits and guinea pigs. He has arrived at conclusions different from those referred to in that he does not regard the liver as

56

parenchyma sleeving blood vessels, or even as columns of parenchymal cells suspended amongst blood vessels. In his view liver substance is composed of solid masses of cells perforated by lacunae which contain the sinusoids: "spaces in which the sinusoids are suspended and separated from one another by walls of hepatic cells. These walls are one cell thick and form a continuous system of anastomosing plates, much like the walls separating the rooms in a building. These rooms, the 'lacunae hepatis' are, however,

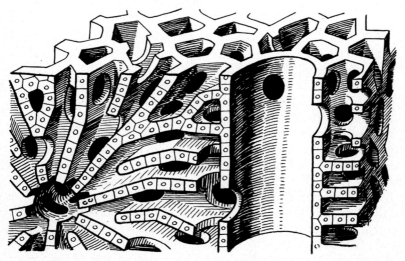

FIG. 5.1. Stereogram of a quadrant of an hepatic lobule. The central space (lower left) runs perpendicularly to the portal space right, which communicates through a few holes with the labyrinth—see text.

(Elias, 1949.)

much taller than wide. Many doors and windows connect them; the walls separating them are crooked, as are the rooms themselves [Fig. 5.1]. Thus, the vast system of these spaces constitutes a labyrinth . . . which pervades, without interruption, entire lobes" (Elias, 1949a). One feature of this approach is to discount old ideas of cords of hepatic tissue; the liver is seen as an integrated structure in which are suspended blood spaces and blood vessels. There is thus probably little real basis for the concept of hepatic units or lobules. The liver masses form a sort of syncytium functioning as a whole.

Externally the liver parenchyma is bounded by a single layer of cells, the external or subcapsular limiting plate (Elias, 1953), which is located under the fibrous capsule and is continuous with the internal plates of the liver. At the porta hepatis the limiting plate bends inwards and follows the branches of the portal vein and hepatic artery, forming a wall under the portal canals (periportal limiting plate). Where the hepatic veins leave the liver, the limiting plate is reflected inwards and again becomes continuous with the internal plate (perihepatic limiting plate).

THE INTRAHEPATIC CIRCULATION

(a) *Sinusoids.* The specialized capillaries of the liver are called sinusoids and are suspended in the lacunae referred to above. It is generally accepted that the wall of the sinusoid is a tube-like arrangement of endothelial cells which has been described as complete (Knisely, 1939; Bloch, 1940; Deysach, 1941) or as perforated at intervals (Mall, 1906; Cameron and Mayes, 1930). Electron microscopy supports the idea that the lining cells are continuous and that they are Küpffer or littoral cells. These cells are flat, irregularly shaped, overlap loosely and are perforated (Ruttner and Vogel, 1957; Wasserman, 1958). Between the littoral cells and the liver cells there is a perisinusoidal space first described by Disse (1890). Within the space is a network of reticulum fibres (Trowell, 1946) which is connected with lymphatic drainage.

It has been noted by several authors that the sinusoids have the power to contract (Knisely, 1939; Wakim and Mann, 1942; Seneviratne, 1949). Wakim and Mann (1942), using a quartz rod illumination technique, claim that about 75 per cent of the hepatic circulation is inactive at any one time, and Seneviratne (1949) considers that contraction and dilatation of sinusoids is one of the methods by which the volume of blood in the liver is regulated. Ruttner and Vogel (1957) claim that bulging Küpffer cells can control the flow at any place in the network of sinusoids.

(b) *The distribution of the portal vein.* At the porta hepatis the portal vein divides into a right and left trunk. It was thought that the right trunk supplied the right lobe of the liver and the left trunk the left lobe. Hjörtso (1951) has shown, however, that the areas of supply of these two branches do not conform strictly to the various lobes of the liver; the right branch supplying by far the larger territory. The right main branch leaves the portal vein at a less acute angle than the left. Blood reaching the bifurcation is divided into two stream lines, the greater amount passing to the right side. The distribution of the intrahepatic branches of the portal vein has been described by Elias (1949). The portal vein in the portal tracts divides into large conducting veins which give rise to small distributing veins, and which run alongside the larger veins. The final branches of the conducting veins and branches from the distributing veins give rise to inlet venules which enter the lobules through holes in the limiting lamina of hepatic cells surrounding the portal tracts and then enter the sinusoids.

Distribution of the hepatic artery

The distribution of the hepatic artery within the liver is controversial. The subject has been reviewed by Hale (1951). It is

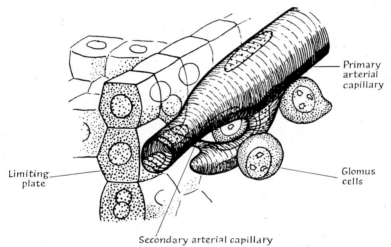

FIG. 5.2. Graphic reconstruction of a secondary arterial capillary arising from a primary arterial capillary and piercing the limiting plate. The cells surrounding the secondary arterial capillary are "glomus" cells—see text.

(Elias, 1949.)

accepted that the artery is distributed to the portal tracts and to a special plexus surrounding the bile ducts. The general plexus surrounding the veins in the portal tract gives rise to branches which supply the tissues of the portal tract (Mall, 1906; Olds and Stafford, 1930; Aunap, 1931), to branches which pass to peripheral sinusoids (Andrews, Maegraith and Wenyon, 1949; Elias, 1949) and to radial sinusoids (Olds and Stafford, 1930; Aunap, 1931). The peribiliary plexus is easily seen in an arterial injection preparation, and branches from it enter the radial sinusoids (Olds and

Stafford, 1930), the peripheral sinusoids (Olds and Stafford, 1930; Andrews *et al.*, 1949; Elias, 1949) and the portal vein. The connections to the portal vein have been described as an arteriolar-venular connection (Cameron and Mayes, 1930; McMichael, 1932) and as a capillary connection (Cameron and Mayes, 1930; Andrews *et al.*, 1949).

The only description of the capillary at the point of entry to the sinusoid is that given by Elias (1949). According to this description there is a localized sphincter-like portion of the capillary at this point where it penetrates the limiting lamina, and in addition there is a group of cells or glomus (Fig. 5.2). This valve-like action is said to be able to close or open to alter flow. Partial contraction will result in high pressure proximally and a jet of blood will be emitted which will be directed to the centre of the lobule.

It should, of course, be realized that these ideas are by no means proven. As will be apparent later they are helpful in the explanation of certain physiological manifestations of the hepatic circulation. Meanwhile there is need for further anatomical verification.

Venous drainage

The gross anatomy of the hepatic veins is fairly straightforward. Kiernan's (1833) original description of the central vein at the axis of the lobule, the sublobular veins and the hepatic veins is valid even today. The hepatic veins are large structures (receiving sinusoidal drainage throughout their length), simple in their branching; in some species such as the dog they are disposed spirally. Their terminal branches are irregular and anastomose occasionally one with the other.

Physiologically speaking, the anatomical feature of the greatest interest is the presence of strong bundles of smooth muscle in the caval ends of the hepatic veins of some species. Simonds (1923) showed that the hepatic veins of the dog contain more smooth muscle than any other species. Popper (1931) in comparison of man, dog and cat found smooth muscle, mainly longitudinal, in the dog which when contracted caused protrusion of the intima into the lumen. Elias and Feller (1931), Arey (1941) and Thomas and Essex (1949) have made similar observations confirming the presence of a sphincter-like mechanism in the dog. In the cat there is little smooth muscle and no evidence of the sort of restriction in the lumen found in the dog. In man the appearances resemble the cat rather than the dog. It must be borne in mind that smooth muscle is a normal constituent of the vein wall, even if there are no sphincters, and it may be difficult to define the point at which a sufficient accumulation of muscle occurs to justify the term "sphincter".

The hepatic venous sphincter has frequently been confused with the "sluice mechanism" described by Deysach in 1941. In his own words ". . . although it is generally stated that liquid enters the liver lobule by way of the portal canals and that liquid is drained from the liver lobule via the central vein, my own observations show that liquid may also drain directly into the sublobular vein via small endothelial tubes (sluice channels) which arise from the confluence of many ordinary sinusoidal capillaries". The "sluice mechanism" is pictured as a mechanism whereby blood may be sequestered in the liver in large quantities, the amount thus sequestered being controlled by the opening or closing of the "sluice valves", namely, the endothelial channels referred to above. If they really exist such channels would act in similar manner to that postulated for the hepatic venous sphincter.

The reality or otherwise of these channels, however, remains to be confirmed. A sluice mechanism is favoured by Chakravati and Tripod (1940) but Seneviratne (1949) was unable to confirm any such structure after a careful search. It seems to be established that the sinusoids themselves are capable of closure (Wakim and Mann, 1942), and it may well be that the appearance of a sluice mechanism in operation might in fact be an artefactual appearance produced by contraction of sinusoids.

ARTERIO-VENOUS COMMUNICATIONS IN THE LIVER

Arteriolar-venular communications as capillary connections between hepatic artery and portal vein have already been referred to. Two other types of anastomosis are possible, namely, veno-venous from the portal vein to the hepatic veins, and arterio-venous from the hepatic artery to the hepatic vein. The former have been identified in mammalian species by Prinzmetal (1948) and his associates, who injected glass spheres, much larger in diameter than capillaries, into the portal vein and recovered them after a moment or so from the lungs. The latter, communications from the hepatic artery to hepatic vein, seem to exist definitely in the amphibian liver, but Wakim and Mann (1942) and Seneviratne (1949) have been unable to demonstrate their presence in mammalian liver.

Hepatic sphincters

A number of sphincter mechanisms have been claimed to exist within the hepatic vasculature, and have been reviewed by Knisely, Harding and Debacker (1957). Sphincters have been described as being pre-sinusoidal along the inlet venules to the peripheral sinusoids, at points of branching of the hepatic artery and where the hepatic artery terminals enter the sinusoids. Post-sinusoidal sphincters are described where the sinusoids drain into the central veins and at the junction of the central veins with the sublobular vein.

VI

METHODS FOR THE MEASUREMENT OR OBSERVATION OF BLOOD FLOW IN THE LIVER

A LARGE variety of techniques have been brought to bear on the problem of hepatic blood flow measurement.

DIRECT FLOW MEASUREMENTS IN THE VESSELS OF SUPPLY

The earliest methods were based on the use of flowmeters applied in the anaesthetized animal to either of the two main vessels supplying the liver. There is no need, here, to recapitulate what has already been said on the subject of flowmeters, except that a great deal of our knowledge is based upon their use. All the devices available for the measurement of flow in cannulated or intact vessels have, at one time or another, been applied to one or both of the main liver vessels. The advantages and disadvantages of these various techniques have already been considered in a previous chapter.

Plethysmographic studies have also been applied to the measurement of changes in liver volume. Most of these methods, applied either to the perfused or the intact liver, involved considerable manipulation. An interesting variant was that of Andrews (1953), who, in his liver perfusion system, estimated volume changes from a modified capsule applied to one surface only of the liver.

PERFUSION STUDIES ON THE ISOLATED ORGAN

The aim of perfusion studies in any organ is to produce a system as near as possible to that obtaining in the living animal in which, however, the parameters of pressure, temperature and blood chemistry can be accurately and independently controlled.

It is well recognized that no perfusion system has yet been devised which really approaches the conditions obtaining in the living animal. In life the hepatic circulation functions as one part of a complex vascular system. There is no doubt that any inter-ference with its circulation seriously affects its subsequent responses and the circulatory dynamics of the isolated liver are very different in many ways from those of the untouched liver. McMichael (1932) has said, ". . . in perfusion experiments on the isolated liver it is well known that after half an hour the pressure in the portal vein must be raised to a level comparable with that in the hepatic artery in order to maintain a flow through the organ".

It must, therefore, be conceded that the circulation in any organ, probably particularly the liver, is very different in the conscious animal as opposed to the isolated organ.

These strictures apart, the use of isolated systems can yield a great deal of knowledge. In some ways it may be argued that such perfusion experiments are no less valid than, say, histological studies which, after all, are made on even less normal tissues, yet whose usefulness has never been questioned. Provided it is borne constantly in mind that what is under examination is an isolated tissue, perfusion experiments can give a great deal of information concerning the responses of the functioning units of the organ to various stimuli.

The work of Bauer, Dale, Poulsson and Richards (1932) is a case in point, and their experimental findings threw a great deal of light on the physiology of the hepatic circulation.

Since their work there have been considerable technical ad-vances. The contributions of Andrews (1953), for example, have come nearer than ever before to the ideal of establishing a per-fusion system without ever depriving the liver of a supply of oxygenated blood. The methods of measurement of flow and volume have also undergone considerable improvement.

BROMSULPHALEIN METHOD OF ESTIMATING MEAN HEPATIC BLOOD FLOW

One of the requirements which has long been acknowledged to be ideal in the measurement of liver blood flow was that there should be a minimum of operative interference and no circulatory impairment of the liver during the preparation of the animal. In this respect, flowmeter techniques (with the possible exception of the thermostromuhr and electromagnetic flowmeter) and perfusion methods are not fully satisfactory. The development of the brom-sulphalein technique by Bradley and his associates (1945) appeared, at first, to be an answer. It was a technique which could be applied to the conscious human subject. There was no interference with liver blood flow at any stage and, compared with the massive trauma of cannulation, very little interference, other than that involved in the passing of a venous catheter into the inferior vena cava.

The method depends on the intravenous infusion of the dye at constant speed, the measurement of dye concentration in the hepatic vein and the measurement of dye concentration in the hepatic artery. Hepatic venous samples are collected by means of a cardiac catheter passed down into the inferior vena cava into a hepatic vein. Peripheral venous blood samples are regarded as identical in their dye concentration with peripheral arterial blood and are withdrawn at the same time as the hepatic venous samples. It is assumed that the liver is the major organ concerned in the removal of bromsulphalein—or at least that the relatively small extrahepatic extraction can be corrected for. Granted either of these assumptions, the Fick formula may be applied to the calculation of hepatic flow.

This method has been applied so extensively that some further consideration must be given to its applicability and to its validity.

The method was devised mainly for human application, but it has also been applied to other species, in particular the dog. It has its technical drawbacks. Cardiac catheterization is a major procedure not to be lightly undertaken. The proper application of the method calls for considerable personal skill, expensive apparatus and for the co-operation of a highly trained team. Moreover rapidly repeated measurements are difficult. Nevertheless, compared with procedures which involve cannulation of vessels it has many advantages in so far as no interference with the liver blood flow is at any time involved. From this point of view it is probably the best of all available methods.

The question of its validity is more difficult to decide, for the technique has had its opponents as well as its protagonists. The crux of the whole matter lies in the manner and extent of extrahepatic extraction of bromsulphalein from circulating blood. Unfortunately it is in this matter that the most widespread disagreement is to be found. Some believe the liver to be the only important organ for extraction; others believe the activity of other tissues is substantial though relatively constant and, in consequence, correctable; yet another body of opinion holds that extrahepatic extraction is so large and so fluctuant as to render the whole technique invalid.

The mechanism of extraction of bromsulphalein is still not clear. Brauer and Prescott (1950) showed that there exist in the body mechanisms for the elimination of acid dyes such as bromsulphalein but that circulatory and structural factors favour dye uptake by the liver in preference to other tissues. In their experiments some of the extracted bromsulphalein was stored in the parenchymal cells, a large proportion was re-excreted in the bile. Most of the excreted bromsulphalein—90 per cent—would seem to be in the form of conjugates which, nevertheless, give the same colour responses as the parent dye (Krebs and Brauer, 1960). Moreover the liver has been shown to be the main organ responsible for the conjugation (Krebs and Brauer, 1958).

Brauer and Prescott (1950) made estimates of the bile excretion, plasma content and total liver content of bromsulphalein. These were compared with the actual amount of bromsulphalein known to have been infused. They concluded on the basis of the discrepancies which appeared that other mechanisms must also be involved in bromsulphalein elimination and claimed that extrahepatic mechanisms might account for 11 to 23 per cent of the total dye extraction (they also considered the possibility that intrahepatic chemical alterations to the dye might be in part responsible for the discrepancies). Selkurt (1953) found an extrahepatic extraction of bromsulphalein of 19 per cent and considered that liver blood flow measured by the bromsulphalein method would have an error of comparable magnitude.

This work tacitly accepts the importance of extrahepatic extraction and implies the need for a correction if the dye method is to be used for practical estimates of liver blood flow or function. Casselman and Rappaport (1954), however, maintained that extrahepatic extraction was negligible. They state "corrections for supposed extrahepatic removal so that results will be in better agreement with other methods seem unwarranted". They base this conclusion on a careful survey of bromsulphalein extraction in various tissues of the dog. Taking the percentage of the dye in the arterial system as 100, they found, for example, an hepatic venous concentration of about 61 per cent, a concentration in the portal vein of 98 per cent, in the femoral vein of 98 per cent, in the renal vein of 97 per cent, and in the jugular vein of 100 per cent.

There can be little doubt that, weight for weight, the liver is far more effective in extracting bromsulphalein than any other tissue. Nevertheless even the figures quoted above indicate some extraction elsewhere; indeed, it would seem that of all the tissues examined only the brain can be said to have no power of dye extraction. Presented in this manner the figures seem suggestive enough but these are, in fact, only figures of blood percentages; in themselves they do not indicate clearance rates, and, until the complete calculation is applied to all the tissues of the body, it is possible that extrahepatic clearance of bromsulphalein may be much higher than these figures at first sight suggest.

Cohn, Levine and Streicher (1947) take a more extreme view. They recovered 31 to 65 per cent of intravenously injected bromsulphalein from the bile. In eviscerated dogs (i.e., dogs with stomach, gastro-intestinal tracts and kidneys removed) they showed that bromsulphalein extraction was maintained at rates of about 20 to 30 per cent of the normal.

This certainly suggests that a considerable degree of extrahepatic extraction is possible. However, Casselman and Rappaport point out with some justice that an eviscerated animal is scarcely normal and that the relatively high extraction rates displayed by tissues forced, as it were, to the task of extraction by the absence of liver, may be very misleading.

Some of the protagonists of the bromsulphalein method concede substantial extrahepatic extraction. They claim, though, that using a high enough rate of intravenous infusion, it is possible to saturate the extrahepatic sites of removal and allow for the figure in the calculation. This is the point of view adopted by Bradley and his co-workers. Cohn, Levine and Kolinsky (1948) investigated the phenomenon of saturation. Even in the totally eviscerated dog the rate of disappearance of bromsulphalein from the blood was roughly three times that for Evans blue. Extrahepatic sites could not be saturated with serum levels as high as 100 mg-% (a serum level far higher than that used in normal measurements even with the so-called high rates of infusion). They suggest that this invalidates the use of the dye for measuring either hepatic blood flow or even maximum transfer capacity since the rate of removal of bromsulphalein is the sum of both the portal and peripheral removal mechanisms.

Werner and Horvath (1952), using dogs, without invoking "saturation" of peripheral sites of removal, adduced evidence to suggest, either with low or with high peripheral serum concentration levels of bromsulphalein, that the extrahepatic clearance was remarkably constant at a level they fixed at about 20 per cent.

Nevertheless all workers do not agree. Sherlock, Bearn, Billing and Paterson (1950), for example, point out that with low serum concentrations arising from low infusion rates, the estimated hepatic blood flow tends to be too high, which suggests a serious error from extrahepatic withdrawal. On the other hand, Inglefinger (1947) suggests that even bigger errors may arise from serum levels which are too high, since there is an upper limit to the ability of the liver to concentrate the dye (Brauer and Prescott, 1950).

Sapirstein (1958*b*) points out a further error which also applies to any method involving sampling from the hepatic vein, namely, that with venous samples taken from a common hepatic vein, estimated hepatic blood flow may be as much as 40 per cent higher than results obtained from a catheter in a deep hepatic vein. The reasons for these discrepancies are complex but it is clear that the precise positioning of the catheter is most important.

Sapirstein states, "We were forced to the conclusion that the dye methods as generally used are, at best, semiquantitative. There is a potential positive error (extrasplanchnic extraction) which may become more significant at low splanchnic blood flow and a potential negative error which is, in all probability, so dependent on the minute details of technique in catheter placement that its magnitude cannot be properly evaluated."

He suggests further that the wide variability in splanchnic flow in the dog may be due to these errors rather than to any biological cause.

Dye clearance methods have so many technical advantages that it is with regret that one has to accept doubts concerning their validity. It would seem, unfortunately, that the conclusions of Sapirstein quoted above must be endorsed and findings obtained with the dye method viewed with caution.

OTHER CLEARANCE METHODS FOR LIVER BLOOD FLOW
MEASUREMENT

1. *Rose Bengal dye method.* The use of Rose Bengal (tetraiodo-tetrachlorfluorescein) was introduced by Simpson, Ezrow and Sapirstein (1954). This is a brilliantly coloured dye at all pH levels in the body. Its presence in tissues is readily detected. It is claimed that the extrahepatic elimination of this dye is very much less than in the case of bromsulphalein. Mean hepatic blood flows obtained by this method are rather lower than those given by the bromsulphalein. It was hoped that the use of this dye would obviate

many of the disadvantages of the bromsulphalein method. However, Sapirstein pointed out that it is subject to the same sampling errors as bromsulphalein, and even if it were more acceptable from the point of view of extrahepatic elimination it would still not constitute a significant technical advance.

2. *Indocyanine green.* The use of the dye indocyanine green has been investigated by Ketterer, Weigland and Rappaport (1960). The estimated hepatic blood flow in the dog gave good agreement with bromsulphalein. The determination in the plasma is easy and it seems that the dye is only removed by the liver. The disadvantages of hepatic vein catheterization still apply.

3. *Isotope tracer methods.* The use of suitable colloids in the estimation of hepatic blood flow was first suggested by Dobson and Jones (1952), who used colloidal chromic phosphate labelled with P^{32}. They observed that such colloids injected into the blood stream disappeared in an exponential manner and showed that the liver and spleen were the only organs involved in this disappearance. The extraction was extremely efficient so that all colloid was removed in one passage through the splanchnic circulation. This means that estimations of hepatic clearance and blood flow can be made from estimations of arterial concentration without the necessity of cannulating the hepatic vein (since the hepatic venous concentration will always be zero).

Radio-gold has similarly been employed by Burkle and Gliedman (1959).

One recent modification of a similar method uses colloidal heat-denatured human serum labelled with I^{131} which enables easy and rapid estimations to be carried out (Shaldon, Chiandusi, Guevera, Caesar and Sherlock, 1961). Some 94 per cent of the labelled albumen is removed by the liver in one passage and, according to Shaldon *et al.*, the method underestimates liver blood flow by about 10 per cent.

The fraction of the cardiac output

Measurement of organ blood flow as a fraction of the cardiac output by means of isotope dilution has been described in Chapter III and has been used to determine liver blood flow by Sapirstein *et al.* (1960).

Urea production and liver blood flow

A method for liver blood determination has been used which

depends on the assumption that all the urea in the urine derives
from the liver and that all the urea liberated by the liver appears
in the urine (Lipscomb and Crandall, 1947). It requires the cannulation of the portal and hepatic veins, the simultaneous determination of urea nitrogen output and the amount of nitrogen added
by the liver to each litre of blood. This method, introduced about
the same time as the bromsulphalein method, required the extra
operative trauma of portal cannulation (or cannulation of a portal
tributary); it was consequently only applicable to animal work and
had little obvious advantage to offer over other methods.

MEASUREMENT OF SPLANCHNIC BLOOD VOLUME

A method for the determination of splanchnic blood volume has
been described by Bradley, Marks, Reynell and Meltzer (1953).
The method resembles other methods of volume measurement in
depending upon the measure of the dilution of a known quantity
of tracer material. A rapid intravenous injection of human serum
albumin labelled with I^{131} is given and frequent arterial and
hepatic venous samples are taken and their activities determined.
The difference between the mean arterial and hepatic venous
radioactivity from zero time to the time when the values are equal
(equilibrium time), multiplied by the hepatic blood flow during
this time gives a value for the total radioactivity dispersed through
the splanchnic bed. The method assumes that there is no collateral
flow, and since the time for equilibration is short, complete mixing
with stored blood (for example, in the spleen) will not occur. The
volume measured is thus the "circulating splanchnic volume".

DIRECT VISUALIZATION OF THE HEPATIC CIRCULATION

Methods which enable the microcirculation of the liver to be
directly observed are, of course, in a rather different category from
what has been discussed. Yet they can be of great value, especially
when considered as complementary to macroscopic observations.

One method used was the serial radiography of Daniel and
Pritchard (1951*a*), who injected radio opaque materials into a
tributary of the portal vein. Subsequent radiographic observations
were used to demonstrate the distribution of blood within the lobes
of the liver. They also studied the course of blood flow through the
liver, vessel diameter and transhepatic circulation time.

The quartz rod technique was another approach used by Knisely (1936), Wakim and Mann (1942) and Seneviratne (1949). It is a direct microscopic technique for the observation of blood flow in vessels down to capillary size. The quartz rod is merely a method transmitting light to the underside of an edge of liver lobe with minimal heating. The method has yielded a great deal of valuable information to which reference will be made later.

Heat transfer techniques

These methods are based on the use of a heated thermocouple. This instrument, introduced by Gibbs (1933), was intended in the first place for the measurement of flow in blood vessels. It consists of a simple thermocouple heated by means of a filament of constantan wire. Increased blood flow cooled the relatively hot thermocouple, decreased flow permitted it to warm up. Used as a flow recorder in blood vessels the technique was limited and subject to many of the faults of the thermostromuhr without sufficient individual advantages to justify it in this context. It was later applied to solid organs by Schmidt and Pearson (1934). In such situations it was used as a qualitative index of flow change. With the recorder *in situ*, a steady heating current was passed. The thermocouple recorded a temperature which depended partly on the current, partly on the movement of blood in the neighbourhood of the thermocouple and on the conductivity of the tissue. An increased blood flow cooled the recorder, a decreased blood flow permitted the temperature to rise.

The technique of "internal calorimetry" was developed by Grayson (1952) and enabled a more quantitative treatment of the findings. In this method thermal conductivity of the liver was measured using a fine-gauge probe inserted into the liver substance. Blood flow produced apparent increments in thermal conductivity (δk) which could be recorded and which protagonists of the method claim to be a linear function of flow in the vicinity of the probe. In animals the probe is inserted at open operation but the animals can recover and survive indefinitely. It can also be applied to conscious human subjects. A full account of the technique and its limitations will be given in the appendix.

Grabner and Neumayr (1958) give details of a thermocouple method which can be applied in man in a different way. A small heating element is fixed to the top of a Cournard catheter which conveys the wires for the temperature and heating circuits. The catheter is introduced into the hepatic vein and a continuous record of temperature obtained. There is no damage to liver tissue, and the method has the advantage that transient changes in hepatic blood flow can be detected. Absolute values for flow are not obtained, but the method is useful for detecting directional changes in flow.

VII

THE CONTROL OF LIVER BLOOD FLOW

CHILD (1954) has said, "Liver as a whole is ever changing insofar as its capacity, its function and its pressure relationships are concerned. Sensitive to the demands of the body as a whole, the liver must today be considered as an organ which plays a dominant role in the control of blood volume, red cell concentration, venous pressure, portal pressure and cardiac output."

Add to this impressive list metabolic functions and the functional demands on the hepatic circulation will be seen to be complex in the extreme. The nature of the problem is further stated in the words of Knisely (1939): ". . . the terminal hepatic arterioles, the arterial sinus twigs, the terminal portal venules, the arterioportal anastomoses, the inlet sphincters, the tubular sinusoidal linings, the outlet sphincters of the sinusoids and of Deysach's sluice channels, the central veins and the sublobular veins are all independently contractile." The difficulty ahead for those who would attempt an easy integrative picture of the hepatic circulation is immediately manifest.

THE MAGNITUDE OF LIVER BLOOD FLOW

Values for liver blood flow obtained by different techniques are shown for the dog, cat and rat in Table 7.1 and for man in Table 7.2. With animals the results have been expressed by various authors as total flow/minute, flow in relation to 100 g liver weight and flow in relation to kg body weight. In man, the results have been expressed as flow/minute, flow/min/square metre of body surface area or in relation to a standard area of 1·73 sq M.

From data published by Selkurt (1953) liver weight has been calculated as 2·82 per cent of body weight for nine dogs of average weight 19·2 kg; from data published by Torrance (1961) the liver weight was 2·26 per cent of body weight (25 dogs, average weight 15·1 kg). For comparison of various data, liver weight, when not supplied by authors, has been taken as 2·5 per cent of body weight for the dog, 1·5 kg for man (*Gray's Anatomy*), 87 g for a 3-kg cat (Barcroft and Shore, 1912) and 4 per cent of body weight for the rat (Bilby, personal communication).

It can be seen from Table 7.1 that for the dog, results obtained

TABLE 7.1

Total hepatic blood flow in animals

Author	Animal	wt/kg	ml./min	ml./100 g liver min	ml./kg body wt min	Method
Burton-Opitz (1911ii)	Dog	16	422	84	26·2	Mechanical stromuhr
Macleod & Pearce (1914)	Dog	10·6	284–620	66–144	27·5–53·5	Outflow collection
Blalock & Mason (1914)	Dog	11·5–18·8	357	82	—	Outflow collection
Grab et al. (1929)	Dog	9·6	279	65	29·0	Thermo-stromuhr
Grindlay et al. (1936)	Dog	16·7	239–538	59–129	14–37	Thermo-stromuhr
Green et al. (1959)	Dog	20·7	429	83	20	Electromagnetic flowmeter
Werner & Horvath (1952)	Dog	16·6	620	149	37·5	Bromsulphalein
Selkurt (1953)	Dog	19·2	677	130	35·4	Bromsulphalein
Smythe et al. (1953)	Dog	18·3	540	117	29·5	Bromsulphalein
Ketterer et al. (1960)	Dog	13·8	510	147	36	Indocyanine green
Smythe (1959)	Dog	—	—	—	38	Chrom-phosphate
Sapirstein & Simpson (1955)	Dog	18·0	577	127	31	Rose Bengal
Schmid (1908)	Cat	3	36	42	12	Stromuhr
Barcroft & Shore (1912)	Cat	3	39	46	15	Outflow collection
Sapirstein et al. (1961)	Rat	0·2	12	142	60	Isotope fractionation
Steiner & Mueller (1961)	Rat	0·2–0·4	8–21	190	42	Isotope fractionation

Average values for animal weights and blood flow are given where possible.

with the mechanical stromuhr, direct outflow collection and the thermostromuhr in terms of flow/liver weight are appreciably lower than those obtained by the bromsulphalein and other clearance methods. The value shown for Green *et al.* (1959) with the electromagnetic flowmeter is also low, but although portal flow was measured by a non-cannulating type meter, the hepatic artery flow was measured in a cannulated vessel and perfused from the femoral artery. Their values for portal flow with the cannulating type flowmeter were so low (77 ml./min) that they rejected such experiments.

When the various species are compared, the flow per 100 g/liver is highest in the rat, followed by the dog, man and cat. Liver blood flow measurements in the cat by modern techniques have not been undertaken.

TABLE 7.2

Hepatic blood flow in man

Author	*ml./min/m²*	*ml./min*	*ml./min/100 g liver*	*Method*
Bradley *et al.* (1945)	870	1500*	100	Bromsulphalein
Myers (1947)	815	1410*	95	Bromsulphalein
Bearn *et al.* (1951)	835	1440*	97	Bromsulphalein
Dobson *et al.* (1953)	1030*	1790	119	Chromphosphate
Caesar (1961)	835	1460	97·5	Indocyanine green
Burkle & Gliedman (1959)	596	1090	72·5	Radio-gold

* Calculated on a surface area of 1·73 m².
Liver weights taken as 1·5 kg.

HUMORAL FACTORS IN THE REGULATION OF LIVER BLOOD FLOW

Effect of adrenaline on liver blood flow

The interpretation of the effects of adrenaline in the intact animal is made difficult by a number of factors. Thus a rise in systemic blood pressure may increase blood flow; vasoconstriction in the gastro-intestinal tract may affect portal inflow; changes in the hepatic arterial inflow may itself affect portal flow in the liver. A rise in portal pressure associated with a decrease in portal flow can be taken, however, to indicate venoconstriction in the portal venous radicles.

Portal vein and arterial radicles

It is generally accepted that adrenaline is constrictor to the radicles of the portal vein and hepatic artery.

Burton-Opitz (1912viii), in his classical experiments on the liver circulation, investigated the effects of adrenaline on liver blood flow in the dog when the drug was injected systemically, and when injected into the hepatic artery and portal vein. Systemic injection of 2–5 minims of adrenaline (1/10,000) in the dog caused a rise in hepatic artery flow of about 15 per cent with a rise in blood pressure of 50 per cent, but when the blood pressure returned to initial levels, hepatic artery flow was reduced by 50–70 per cent. When the adrenaline was injected into the hepatic artery, there was little rise in blood pressure, but hepatic artery pressure rose by 15 mm

Hg and flow fell by 38 per cent. It was clear that adrenaline constricted branches of the hepatic artery. Injection of adrenaline into the portal vein in somewhat larger doses (8–15 minims), with the hepatic artery ligated, resulted in an initial rise in portal pressure of 2–5 times the initial value and a decreased portal inflow of about 20 per cent. Blood pressure and portal inflow then rose and portal pressure remained elevated. When the blood pressure returned to initial levels portal inflow fell again and portal pressure remained elevated. Burton-Opitz concluded that adrenaline was constrictor to portal venous radicles but the effects were less marked than on the hepatic arterial branches. These results were substantially confirmed by Macleod and Pearce (1914) in the dog using the direct outflow collection from the hepatic veins. Thus 2 ml. of 1/10,000 adrenaline injected into the pancreatico-duodenal vein when the hepatic artery was intact reduced flow by 22 per cent, but when the hepatic artery was ligated, the reduction in flow was only 10·5 per cent.

Subsequent work has largely confirmed the findings of Burton-Opitz. Thus, McMichael (1932) examined the effect of adrenaline on portal venous pressure and liver volume *in situ* in the cat. He found that adrenaline had a constrictor action on the ramifications of the portal vein, but that portal venous pressure showed a secondary rise because of an increased flow of blood through the hepatic and mesenteric arteries as a result of the rise in systemic blood pressure.

In an attempt to overcome the difficulties associated with changes in gastro-intestinal inflow a number of studies have been made with the perfused isolated liver. Bauer, Dale, Poulsson and Richards (1932) found that adrenaline constricted portal venous and hepatic arterial radicles in the dog, cat and goat. The reduction in portal venous inflow with 5 μg adrenaline injected into the portal vein of the dog was about 11 per cent. The effect was large in the cat but very small in the goat. Absolute values were not given. Similar results have been found by Chakravati and Tripod (1940) and Andrews, Hecker, Maegraith and Ritchie (1955) for perfused dog livers, and Andrews, Hecker, Maegraith (1956) for monkeys, cats and rabbits.

An assessment of the relative effectiveness of adrenaline on the portal venous and hepatic arterial circulation has been made by Green *et al.* (1959). Portal flow was measured by non-cannulating type electromagnetic flowmeters and hepatic artery flow by a cannulating type flowmeter, the hepatic artery being perfused by diverted femoral artery blood. When 10 μg adrenaline were injected into the hepatic artery, flow fell in one experiment from 62·5 ml./min to zero and then rose to 87·5 ml./min. Portal venous pressure rose from 7·5 mm Hg to 9·1 mm Hg and portal flow increased slightly from 540 ml./min to 585 ml./min. When a similar dose of adrenaline was injected into the portal vein, hepatic artery flow fell from 62·5 ml./min to 11·0 ml./min and then rose to 84·0 ml./min. Portal flow rose from 559 ml./min to 650 ml./min and then fell to 533 ml./min. Portal pressure rose from 8·8 mm Hg to 13·8 mm Hg and then fell to 8·2 mm Hg. The changes in portal flow were related to changes in systemic blood pressure and possibly to altered resistance to inflow by a reduction of hepatic arterial inflow. Calculations of resistance show an increase of 400–600 per cent for the hepatic artery, and 125–200 per cent for the portal vein, and they conclude that the arterial circuit is more responsive to adrenaline than the portal venous circuit. The results are in agreement with Burton-Opitz (1912viii) and Macleod and Pearce (1914).

Fischer and Takacs (1962) measured hepatic artery flow in the dog with a rotameter and found that 3 μg/min of adrenaline injected into the hepatic artery resulted in a rise of blood pressure of about 20 mm Hg and a rise in hepatic artery flow from 110 ml./min to 150 ml./min. They claim that adrenaline reduced the resistance to hepatic arterial flow. From haemodynamic considerations referred to in a previous chapter it is clear that in experiments where pressure and flow change in the same direction, apparent changes in resistance may occur passively. It is doubtful whether the observations of Fischer and Takacs can really be interpreted as indicating an active reduction in resistance to hepatic arterial flow. In any case baroreceptor mechanisms arising from the change in systemic blood pressure were not excluded.

In general available evidence shows that adrenaline is constrictor to the portal venous and hepatic arterial radicles. Through its effect on systemic blood pressure it may, despite this, bring about an increase in flow through these channels.

Sinusoids

Contraction of the sinusoids of the liver with adrenaline has been reported by Wakim (1944) in frog and rat liver using the quartz rod transillumination technique. These findings have been confirmed by Seneviratne (1949), using a similar technique in the rat.

Hepatic veins

The early literature describing the effect of adrenaline on the hepatic veins appears to be contradictory, probably the main reason being that the importance of dose was not fully appreciated. Thus, Baer and Roessler (1926), perfusing dog liver from the vena cava, showed that adrenaline caused hepatic venous constriction. Similar results were obtained by Simonds and Brandes (1929). Mautner (1924) produced results which appeared to differ. Following up previous observations by Mautner and Pick (1915) in which it had been shown that histamine produced swelling of the liver, Mautner now showed that adrenaline prevented this swelling, a finding he interpreted as due to dilatation of the hepatic veins. Grab, Jansen and Rein (1929), using the thermostromuhr in the dog, showed that adrenaline regularly caused the hepatic venous outflow to exceed the inflow, as much as 59 per cent of the weight of the bloodless liver leaving it during the period of excessive outflow.

Bauer, Dale, Poulsson and Richards (1932) amply demonstrated the importance of this phenomenon in experiments on the isolated perfused dog liver (Fig. 7.1). Adrenaline in doses of 20 μg injected into the hepatic artery led to a fall in portal inflow, liver volume and outflow from the liver. Adrenaline in doses of 2 μg produced marked diminutions in portal inflow and in liver volume but caused an increase in outflow from the liver. Adrenaline in doses of 5 μg injected into the portal vein had similar effects. Bauer *et al.* went further. They incised the hepatic veins, cutting the muscle coats to abolish contractility. After this procedure adrenaline always caused reduction in portal outflow in whatever dose it was given.

The dilating effect of adrenaline in small doses on hepatic veins has been confirmed in the perfused dog liver by Chakravati and Tripod (1940) and by Andrews *et al.* (1955).

In a similar series of experiments performed on the cat and goat by Bauer *et al.* (1932) no evidence was obtained of increase in hepatic venous outflow ever occurring with adrenaline.

These experiments led to the postulate that in the dog the hepatic venous outflow is controlled by a physiologically active sphincter. The anatomical basis for such a mechanism has already been described. In species where this mechanism exists, it clearly provides the basis for blood storage functions within the liver. A liver contracting under the influence of adrenaline with open sphincters would be expected to produce increased outflow with diminished volume and diminished inflow.

It should, however, be clearly borne in mind that such a mechanism has only been clearly demonstrated in the dog. Smooth muscle is a normal constituent of the vein wall of all species, but in

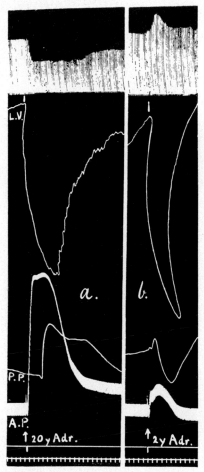

FIG. 7.1. Perfused dog liver. Upper trace—hepatic venous outflow; L.V.—liver volume; P.P.—portal pressure; A.P.—arterial pressure. A large dose of adrenaline injected into the hepatic artery produced a fall in venous outflow accompanied by a reduction in liver volume. A small dose of adrenaline produced a rise in hepatic venous outflow which was still accompanied by a reduction in liver volume.

(Bauer, Dale, Poulsson and Richards, 1932.)

varying amounts, and it is doubtful if so well developed a sphincter mechanism as found in the dog exists in any other species including man.

Effect of adrenaline on total liver blood flow

The observation of Burton-Opitz (1912viii) that changes in blood pressure with systemically administered adrenaline could cause an increase in portal flow and hence in liver blood flow was confirmed by McLaughlin (1928) in the rabbit. Grayson and Johnson (1953), using internal calorimetry in the rabbit, similarly observed that liver thermal conductivity (blood flow) increased with the rise in blood pressure, but that injections of adrenaline into the portal vein reduced liver blood flow.

Ginsburg and Grayson (1954) claimed that the increase in liver blood flow with a rise in systemic blood pressure was not purely

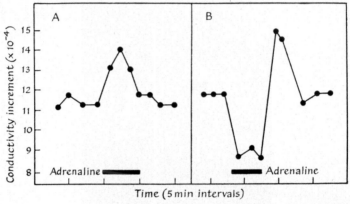

FIG. 7.2. The effect of coeliac neurectomy on the liver blood flow response (conductivity increment) to intravenous infusion of adrenaline in conscious rats. (A) Before coeliac neurectomy; (B) 24 hours after coeliac neurectomy.

(Ginsburg and Grayson, 1954.)

mechanical, but that there was a vasodilator response mediated by the baroreceptors. Using the technique of internal calorimetry in the liver of the rat they showed that the rise in liver blood flow associated with increased blood pressure could be partially prevented by coeliac neurectomy (Fig. 7.2) or by ganglion blockade with tetraethyl ammonium bromide 10 mg/kg/i.v. (Fig. 7.3). The dilator effect did not appear to be due to the removal of sympathetic activity for it could also be abolished by atropine (5 mg/kg/i.v.). It was concluded that there was a cholinergic efferent pathway. The implication of baroreceptor mechanisms was shown by experiments in the rabbit in which blood pressure was recorded from the left carotid artery and the right depressor nerve sectioned.

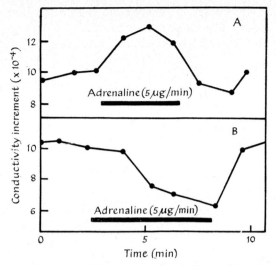

FIG. 7.3. The effect of intravenous adrenaline on blood flow (conductivity increment) in the rat liver. Ether anaesthesia. (A) before; (B) after the administration of tetraethyl ammonium bromide (10 mg/kg/i.v.).

(Grayson and Johnson, 1953.)

When the right carotid was clamped (which they considered inactivated the sinus baroreceptor on that side) and adrenaline infused, there was a rise in liver blood flow and blood pressure. When the remaining depressor nerve was sectioned, adrenaline infusion now produced a fall in liver blood flow and a rise in blood pressure (Fig. 7.4). They considered that provided one baroreceptor mechanism was left intact the response could be elicited. Their evidence, however, is not conclusive since clamping the carotid arteries with the sinus nerves intact does not completely inactivate the carotid sinus baroreceptors because of anastomotic channels between the sinus and other arteries. In conjunction with other evidence, however, it does suggest a measure of baroreceptor control of the hepatic circulation.

In man, Bradley *et al.* (1945) showed that adrenaline infusion led to an increase in liver blood flow. In a more detailed study by Bearn *et al.* (1951), adrenaline infusion at a rate of 0·1 μg/kg/min produced increases in liver blood flow estimated by bromsulphalein of from 20 to 180 per cent and decreases in resistance of about 60 per cent. There was an increased glucose output by the liver and an increased oxygen uptake. They concluded that adrenaline infusions resulted in splanchnic vasodilatation. Grayson and Kinnear (1962) used internal calorimetry to measure the effect of adrenaline

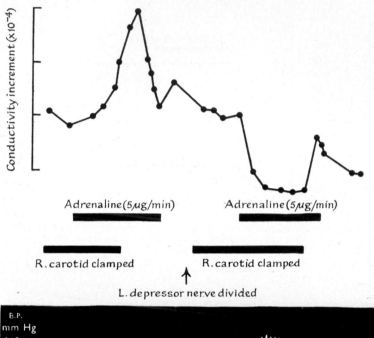

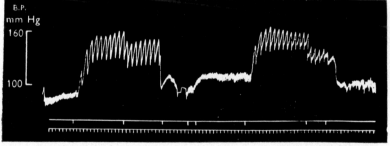

FIG. 7.4. The influence of the carotid sinuses and depressor nerves on reflex blood flow (conductivity increment) responses to adrenaline (5 μg/min intravenously) in the rabbit liver. Blood pressure recording from the left carotid artery. Right depressor nerve cut before the record was taken. Time interval 30 sec.

(Grayson and Johnson, 1953.)

on liver blood flow in man. In many experiments there was little change in systemic blood pressure; in such experiments reductions in liver blood flow occurred. In other experiments substantial increments in systemic blood pressure occurred accompanied by elevations in blood flow. They considered that in man, as in other animals, the effect of any given dose of adrenaline will be the resultant on the one hand of a direct vasoconstrictive effect, on the other hand of the increased perfusion pressure and possibly, too, of baroreceptor initiated vasodilator mechanisms.

Whatever the mechanism, it is clear from the weight of evidence that the usual response of the liver vasculature to systemically administered adrenaline is a net increase in flow although the direct effect of adrenaline on liver blood vessels appears to be vasoconstrictor.

Effect of noradrenaline

The qualitative responses of the liver to noradrenaline appear to be much the same as those for adrenaline. Thus, in perfused dog livers Andrews *et al.* (1955) showed that it was constrictor to both portal venous and hepatic arterial radicles—also in rabbit, cat and monkey. Its action on the hepatic vein was, like adrenaline, dilator with the qualification that its dilator action was even more evident than that of adrenaline. Grayson and Johnson (1953), using internal calorimetry in the rabbit, found that noradrenaline ($10 \mu g/min$) was a more powerful vasoconstrictor than adrenaline, a fall in liver blood flow occurring with a rise in blood pressure. Smythe, Gilmore and Handford (1954) measured liver blood flow in the dog by the bromsulphalein technique and were unable to detect a change in blood flow with noradrenaline, although there was an increase in splanchnic oxygen consumption and splanchnic vascular resistance, suggesting that vasoconstriction was such as to prevent the effects of a mechanical rise in blood pressure. Bearn *et al.* (1951) have shown that in man, noradrenaline ($0\cdot1-0\cdot2 \mu g/kg/min$) causes a reduction in hepatic blood flow and an increase in splanchnic vascular resistance (Fig. 7.5). In these experiments systolic blood pressure rose from 24–100 mm Hg and diastolic pressure 20–70 mm Hg, so that the drop in blood flow associated with a rise in perfusion pressure was probably the result of active vasoconstriction.

Green *et al.* (1959) measured portal venous flow and hepatic artery flow in dogs with electromagnetic flowmeters and found that 10 μg noradrenaline produced similar effects to adrenaline but of less magnitude. Fischer and Takacs (1962) found that infusion of noradrenaline ($3 \mu g/min$) into the hepatic artery of dogs reduced hepatic artery flow, measured by a rotameter, by 50 per cent, whereas a similar dose of adrenaline increased flow.

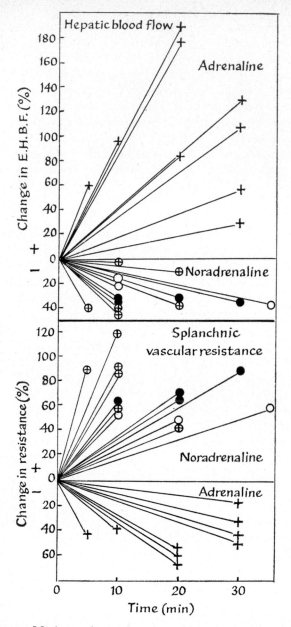

Fig. 7.5. Maximum changes in estimated hepatic blood flow (brom-sulphalein method) and splanchnic vascular resistance in man during infusions of adrenaline and noradrenaline. Time 0 refers to beginning of infusion. +——+, adrenaline 0·10 μg/kg/min. ●——●, noradren-aline, 0·10 μg/kg/min. ○——○, noradrenaline 0·15 μg/kg/min. ⊕——⊕, noradrenaline 0·20 μg/kg/min. (Bearn *et al.*, 1951.)

There is, then, general agreement that noradrenaline is vasoconstrictor to the hepatic vasculature. Most of the evidence suggests
that it is probably more powerful in this respect than adrenaline since its effect on actual flow in the liver when administered
systemically was to reduce it even when there was a substantial
concomitant rise in arterial pressure.

Effect of acetylcholine

The evidence regarding the effect of acetylcholine on liver blood
flow is contradictory, and is again complicated by the effects of
acetylcholine on the systemic circulation.

Bauer *et al.* (1932) injected 20 μg acetylcholine into the hepatic
artery of the perfused dog liver. The results were not consistent,
but if arterial tone was high there was occasionally relaxation of the
vessel.

The effects on the portal radicles of the dog were uncertain. With
the cat liver, acetylcholine dilated the hepatic artery, but with the
goat liver both the hepatic artery and portal radicles were constricted. In other experiments with perfused dog livers, Chakravati
and Tripod (1940) found that 10 μg of acetylcholine injected into
the hepatic artery caused an increase of liver volume of about 10 ml.,
and a drop in outflow of about 40 per cent. This diminution in outflow did not occur when the acetylcholine was injected into the
portal vein although the volume of the liver still increased. This
effect was not easy to explain; however, they concluded that, since
there appeared to be a reciprocal linkage between hepatic artery
and portal vein, a dilatation in the hepatic artery would lead to the
opposite effect in the portal radicles. They concluded therefore that
acetylcholine increases hepatic arterial flow and, in consequence of
this rather obscure mechanism, reduces portal flow leading to a net
diminution in outflow. Acetylcholine thus appeared to dilate both
the hepatic arterial and portal venous radicles, although the effect
on the portal venous radicles was less than on the hepatic artery.
Andrews *et al.* (1955) found that acetylcholine (0·25–15 μg) dilated
the hepatic artery in the perfused dog liver when the artery was
constricted, but also regularly constricted the hepatic vein and
occasionally the portal vein. The effect on the portal vein was more
marked if the drug was injected into the hepatic arterial circulation, but if eserine was added to the perfusion fluid, the effects were
similar if injected into the hepatic artery or portal vein.

In the cat, with liver volume measured *in situ*, McMichael (1933) found that doses of acetylcholine (0·2–0·5 mg) caused a rise in portal pressure by constriction of the portal vein. With smaller doses (0·001–0·2 mg), there was no direct action on the vein but portal pressure fell and then rose. The fall in portal pressure was considered due to the fall in cardiac output, and the fall in splanchnic

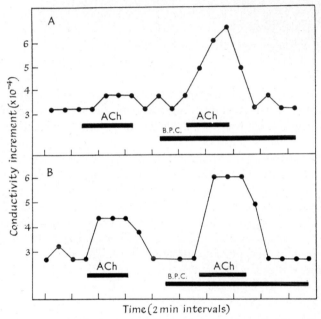

FIG. 7.6. The effect of acetylcholine infusion (5 μg/min) on liver blood flow (conductivity increment) in the rat, with and without blood pressure compensation. Portal circulation to liver excluded. (A) before hexamethonium; (B) after hexamethonium (5 mg/kg i.v.). B.P.C.—blood pressure compensation.

(Ginsburg and Grayson, 1954.)

blood flow; the rise in portal pressure to constriction of the portal venules. The rise could be abolished by ergot, however, and he considered the effect to be due to activation of the sympathetics. Katz and Rodbard (1939) measured portal blood flow and hepatic venous outflow by the mechanical stromuhr in dogs. Acetylcholine produced a fall in portal and systemic arterial pressures which led to secondary mechanical falls in liver blood flow. Wakim (1944) found that acetylcholine had little effect on the sinusoids of transilluminated livers of the frog and rat. Large doses led to a fall in blood pressure and a decreased flow through the sinusoids. Seneviratne (1949) found on the other hand that acetylcholine constricted liver sinusoids in the transilluminated rat liver, followed by dilatation and stagnation. Grayson and Ginsburg (1954) measured liver blood flow in the rat by internal calorimetry. The portal circulation was excluded. Acetylcholine infusion (5 μg/min) caused a small increase in liver blood flow, but if the blood pressure was kept constant by means of transfusion of blood from a reservoir, there was an appreciable increase in blood flow (Fig. 7.6). After administration of a ganglion blocking agent, hexamethonium bromide (5 mg/kg/i.v.), acetylcholine produced a marked rise in liver blood flow both with or without blood pressure compensation (Fig. 7.6 B). They suggested that acetylcholine was a vasodilator agent, but that the effects could be obscured by a fall in blood pressure and in part by vasoconstrictor reflexes, possibly baroreceptor in mediation. Green *et al.* (1959) found that 10 μg acetylcholine injected into the hepatic artery of the dog increased hepatic artery flow and decreased resistance. A similar amount of acetylcholine injected into the portal vein increased portal venous pressure and flow but with little change in resistance. Fischer and Takacs (1962) found a 65 per cent increase in hepatic arterial flow in the dog, measured by a rotameter, with an injection of 5–7·5 μg acetylcholine into the hepatic artery. It seems then to be established that acetylcholine is markedly vasodilator to the branches of the hepatic artery. Its effect on the portal venous radicles is less certain but is probably mildly vasodilator. Its effect on total liver blood flow is variable and depends on these actions together with the systemic effects on the liver circulation of lowered blood pressure.

Effect of histamine on hepatic blood flow

The observations of Mautner and Pick (1915) on the perfused dog liver brought to notice a mechanism (the Sperre mechanism) controlling the outflow of blood from the hepatic veins and on which histamine had a powerful constrictor effect. Baer and Roessler (1926) confirmed the constrictor effect of histamine but considered the smaller radicles of the hepatic veins to be the vessels concerned. Bauer *et al.* (1932), in the perfused dog liver, showed that histamine caused a constriction of portal radicles, a marked reduction of hepatic vein outflow and an increase in liver volume. In one experiment, 3 μg of histamine reduced outflow by 69 ml./min and inflow by 27 ml./min. Histamine did not affect outflow in the goat or cat, however, and the cat was particularly insensitive to the constrictor effect of histamine on the portal branches.

Bauer *et al.* (1932) considered that histamine was critically concerned in the control of the hepatic venous outlet sphincters. They maintained that the function of such sphincters was probably to cause the accumulation of blood in the liver during digestion and that small amounts of histamine liberated from the gastrointestinal tract were the effective agency involved. On the other hand, opening up of the sphincters in response to such calls as muscular activity, requiring the mobilization of the floating reserves of the blood, would be effected by adrenaline and sympathetic impulses. They remarked, "... the whole mechanism, indeed, when thus considered, appears to be so well adapted to adjustment of the current blood volume to the body's needs, that failure to find it in other species is more surprising than its discovery in the dog". It may well be relevant that according to Parratt and West (1957) the dog liver contains almost 24 times the amount of histamine per unit weight as the livers of cats or rodents and 8 times the amount of histamine as the rabbit.

Nevertheless, it must be remembered the dog is by no means typical as regards its portal circulation. Thus, Bradley and Inglefinger (1952) in man, using the bromsulphalein technique, found that 0·4–0·6 mg of histamine phosphate intramuscularly resulted in a sharp fall in blood pressure accompanied by a slight increase in liver blood flow. They could find no evidence for a restriction of liver blood flow.

It must be concluded that the action of histamine is species variable. In the dog it may well have a crucial role to play in the control of hepatic venous sphincters and blood storage in the liver. In other species it has little effect and may even be vasodilator in man.

NERVOUS FACTORS IN THE CONTROL OF LIVER BLOOD FLOW

(1) *Sympathetic vasoconstrictor fibres*

It is generally agreed that the sympathetic nervous system supplies vasoconstrictor fibres to the hepatic artery and portal venous radicles. Pal (1888) reported that stimulation of the splanchnic nerves of the dog resulted in an increased hepatic venous outflow from the liver. The effect seemed to originate within the liver since there was a small flow of blood with each stimulation even when the portal and arterial inflows were obstructed. His findings were confirmed by Mall (1892). Bayliss and Starling (1894*b*) showed that the liver received a sympathetic innervation via the splanchnic nerves and the coeliac ganglion from the 3rd to the 9th thoracic segments, and found that stimulation of the splanchnic nerves produced a rise in portal pressure.

Francois-Franck and Hallion (1897), in their classical work on the liver circulation, measured liver volume and hepatic artery and portal vein pressures. They obtained evidence in the dog that splanchnic nerve stimulation resulted in a rise in portal and hepatic artery pressures and a shrinkage of the liver. They also noted a rise in pressure in the inferior vena cava at the level of entry of the hepatic veins and interpreted this as a squeezing out of blood by contraction of the hepatic veins.

Burton-Opitz (1912v) confirmed that splanchnic stimulation contracted the hepatic arterial radicles. At first he failed to confirm that splanchnic nerve stimulation had an effect on the portal radicles. He found a rise in portal pressure but also a rise in portal flow and attributed it to a rise in general arterial pressure. He later found that when the portal vein was perfused under constant pressure, splanchnic nerve stimulation constricted the veins, but he considered the effect less marked than on the arterial circulation. Macleod and Pearce (1914) found that stimulation of the hepatic plexus in the dog increased hepatic vein outflow by 5–60 per cent. They interpreted this as vasoconstriction but found the effect less marked if the hepatic artery was occluded and were thus in agreement with Burton-Opitz. Griffith and Emery (1930) measured liver volume *in situ* in the cat. Stimulation of post-ganglionic fibres along the hepatoduodenal artery or pre-ganglionic fibres of the splanchnic nerves gave a reduction of liver volume. Bauer *et al.* (1932) also found that stimulation of the hepatic nerves led to hepatic arteriolar vasoconstriction in dog liver; they also found that hepatic nerve stimulation caused an increase in hepatic venous outflow, due presumably to relaxation of the outflow sphincters.

From angiographic studies, Daniel and Pritchard (1951*b*) have obtained direct evidence of constriction of the portal tree in the cat and dog on stimulation of hepatic nerves (Fig. 7.7). Green *et al.* (1959) showed clearly that stimulation of the left greater splanchnic nerve increased both hepatic arterial and portal venous pressures. Portal venous flow fell from 77 ml./min to 22·5 ml./min, and hepatic artery flow from 153 ml./min to 64 ml./min. (The low portal flow was due to cannulation of the portal vein for the insertion of an electromagnetic flowmeter in this experiment.) Calculation of resistance gave a 175 per cent increase for the hepatic artery and 225 per cent increase for the portal vein, the converse of the results with adrenaline.

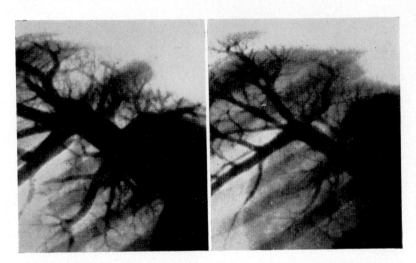

FIG. 7.7. Individual angiograms in the dog showing constriction of the intrahepatic vessels of the portal tree which occurs after electrical stimulation of the distal end of the divided hepatic plexus of nerves. Left-hand figure; before stimulation. Right-hand figure; after stimulation.

(Daniel and Pritchard, 1951*b*.)

It is thus agreed that the sympathetic nerve supply to the liver is markedly vasoconstrictor to the hepatic arterial radicles. It is probably also constrictor to the portal venous radicles. Its effect on the hepatic veins may be different for there is evidence to show that where sphincters exist they are relaxed by sympathetic activity. Sympathetically mediated vasoconstriction is, however, less evident in the liver than in the mesenteric bed where nerve stimulation has been shown by Green *et al.* to raise the resistance by 500 per cent.

(2) *Hepatic vasodilator nerves*

The question of hepatic vasodilator nerves to the liver is more controversial. We have already considered the effect of acetylcholine and concluded that it can produce vasodilatation in the liver. Francois-Franck and Hallion (1896) claimed that an increase in hepatic volume occurred with vagal stimulation. Grab, Jansen and Rein (1929), using the thermostromuhr, claimed an increase in liver blood flow of the dog after atropine and that the vagus exerted a tonic control of the hepatic veins. Griffith and Emery (1930) were unable to demonstrate an effect on liver volume in the cat of vagal stimulation, and Bauer *et al.* (1932) could find no evidence of vagal dilator fibres in the liver of the dog perfused *in situ*. Grayson and Johnson (1953) claimed to have demonstrated dilator fibres to the liver of the rabbit. They measured liver blood flow by internal calorimetry, and found that when the depressor nerves were stimulated and the blood pressure prevented from changing there was an increase in liver blood flow. They reached similar conclusions from experiments in the rat in which they stimulated the intact vagus and prevented blood pressure change. The increase in liver blood flow so obtained was abolished by coeliac neurectomy or the administration of atropine.

Green *et al.* (1959), however, could find no evidence of sympathetic cholinergic vasodilators in the hepatic bed of the dog. Furthermore there was no evidence of vasodilatation following blockade with ilidar. Iso-propyl noradrenaline did not lead to vasodilatation so it may be concluded that the hepatic vascular bed does not contain any adrenergic dilator receptors (β receptors).

No final answer is possible in view of the conflicting evidence. Species variation is possible as an explanation of some of the disagreement. Meanwhile the best that can probably be said is that the possibility of parasympathetic vasodilator fibres to the liver has not been excluded.

BARORECEPTOR REFLEXES AND RESTING VASOMOTOR TONE IN THE LIVER

Reference has already been made to the possible participation of baroreceptor mechanisms in the overall action on liver blood flow of humoral agents which also alter the systemic blood pressure. There is little doubt, in fact, that the hepatic bed can participate in generalized splanchnic responses to altered blood pressure. As long ago as 1897 Francois-Franck and Hallion showed that lowering the blood pressure caused vasoconstriction in the liver. They also showed that stimulation of the central end of the cut vagus increased liver volume. Griffith and Emery (1930), in the cat, showed that sciatic stimulation which affected the blood pressure

variably had also an effect on liver blood flow. Thus, when the
blood pressure rose, liver volume decreased; when the blood pressure
sure fell, liver volume increased. These effects were abolished by
section of post-ganglionic sympathetic fibres and were in agreement
ment with the observations of Francois-Franck and Hallion.

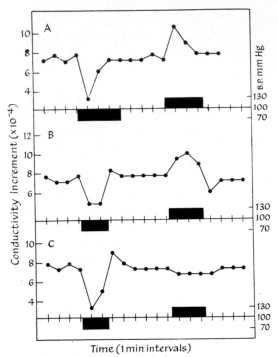

FIG. 7.8. Effects of vagus nerve section on liver blood flow (conductivity increment) responses to mechanically induced changes in blood
pressure in the rat. B.P. maintained at 100 mm Hg except for reductions to 70 mm Hg (solid blocks below line) and elevation to 130 mm
Hg (solid blocks above line). (A) before nerve section; (B) after left
vagus nerve section; (C) after right and left vagus nerve section.
(Ginsburg and Grayson, 1954.)

Gollwitzer-Meier and Schulte (1931) measured liver blood flow
in the dog and also showed that when there was an increase in
carotid sinus pressure there was an increase in liver volume. Ginsburg and Grayson (1954) showed that in the rat (Fig. 7.8) artificially
induced falls or increments in blood pressure also brought about
falls or increments in liver blood flow (which could be greatly reduced by ganglion blockade or by vagal nerve section).

The undoubted vasoconstrictor propensities of the sympathetic nerve supply to the liver, the generally agreed participation of the hepatic blood vessels in baroreceptor responses offer a ready basis for assuming the likelihood of vasomotor tone in the liver. Griffith and Emery considered the effects they observed to be due to inhibition or enhancement of vasomotor tone in the liver.

Nevertheless there is some doubt as to whether such tone does or does not exist in the liver. Ginsburg and Grayson (1954) could find no definite effect on liver blood flow in the conscious rat after administration of an adrenolytic agent, dibenzyline. Green *et al.* (1959) could find no definite effects after blockade with ilidar in the dog and Fischer (1963) found only transient effects in the dog with dibenamine, 8 mg/kg. On the other hand, Billington, Paton, Reynolds and Sherlock (1954), using the bromsulphalein technique in man, showed that ganglion blockade caused an increase in flow suggesting the existence of vasomotor tone.

Again there can be no general answer. Species variations are a possible factor involved in the differences. Despite the undoubted activity of the sympathetic nerves and the ability of the hepatic vessels to participate in baroreceptor effects, the presence of vasomotor tone must be regarded as non-proven.

STORAGE FUNCTIONS OF THE LIVER

The liver is frequently referred to as an organ of blood storage. It has been stated that in about 75 per cent of the liver substance, the circulation, under ordinary circumstances, is inactive, its sinusoids being packed with red cells and apparently serving as storage depots (Wakim and Mann, 1942).

This statement implies that the liver stores blood in much the same way that the spleen has been demonstrated to store blood. That is to say, blood is sequestered in sinusoids which during the period of storage are cut off from the main stream of the circulation. It is implied further that blood thus stored can be given up to the general circulation when required, as for example in haemorrhage, or conversely, that blood can be withdrawn from the general circulation and taken into storage.

We must, however, clearly differentiate between this kind of storage and changes in hepatic volume brought about by contraction or relaxation of its vascular elements—including in this phrase, not merely the microcirculation of arterioles, capillaries, sinusoids and venules, but also the hepatic sphincters. Alterations brought about by simple vasoactive responses might well have a marked effect on systemic blood pressure regulation, they may also produce marked changes in liver volume, but they are not necessarily related to changes in blood storage capacity.

Evidence for blood storage in the liver really depends on two types of observation. In the first place there are the quite remarkable changes which may occur in liver volume; secondly there are the microscopic observations of Knisely (1939), who observed directly the behaviour of liver sinusoids.

There can be little doubt that increased resistance to venous outflow can greatly increase liver volume. Gollwitzer-Meier and Eckhart (1934), for example, showed an increased vena-caval pressure to have marked effect. Andrews, Hecker, Maegraith and Ritchie (1955) showed, in the isolated dog liver, that spasm of the hepatic veins could produce a very considerable increase in liver volume. Such mechanisms, indeed, lead to the withholding of considerable volumes of blood from the general circulation. Nevertheless this is not storage in the sense in which the word is here applied, it is venous stasis, and in the first place merely the partial retention of whole blood not merely in the liver but in the whole venous side of the splanchnic circulation.

The sequelae of such venous retention may well be relevant since there is evidence to suggest that the second stage of venous retention of this kind is a slowing of blood flow in the sinusoids and, by a process of fluid absorption, concentration of cells within the sinusoids.

The effect of adrenaline on the liver vasculature and volume has already been discussed. Small doses reduce liver volume and dilate the hepatic venous sphincters of the dog. Large doses, however, have been shown by Bainbridge and Dale (1905) to cause swelling of the liver; Bainbridge and Trevan (1917) showed further that large doses of adrenaline caused "pooling" of blood in the splanchnic area, a phenomenon which they associated with the onset of "adrenaline shock".

Whether or not the liver is thus critically implicated in adrenaline or any other kind of shock the fact remains that livers of all species have a high labile vascular capacity irrespective of whether or not sphincters exist on the hepatic venous outflow. Ludwig (1932), for example, claimed that the human liver has a labile vascular capacity of 1 to 2 litres, i.e. that this volume of blood may be stored in the liver or liberated into the general circulation. Sjöstrand (1934) claimed that 20 per cent of the blood volume could be held in the liver. The quantitative importance of changes in liver volume have been emphasized by Katz and Rodbard (1939), who state "considerations of the fact that the liver may hold as much as 35 per cent of the total blood volume and that the preportal bed holds another 30 per cent places proper emphasis upon the quantitative importance of this system. The hepato-portal system is thus truly 'the venesector and blood giver of the circulatory system'."

In the literal sense of the word the above does not really demonstrate blood storage. The argument may appear to be merely semantic since it is abundantly clear that substantial alterations in liver volume and the volume of the hepato-portal vascular bed can occur. Nevertheless there is a difference between a mechanism which acts by altering the capacity of the vascular bed and one which enables blood to be sequestered away from the main stream, stored and concentrated.

That blood can be completely static in the liver sinusoids is suggested by Knisely (1939) and Wakim and Mann (1942), who observed the microcirculation in the edge of the liver and concluded that a large proportion of the sinusoids were inactive at any one time and contained truly sequestered blood. Moreover the concept of sinusoids as blood stores fits well with Deysach's "sluice mechanism" hypothesis.

The observations of Barcroft, Nisimaru and Ray (1932) are, however, against the idea of a vascular "*cul-de-sac*" in the liver. They showed that the time taken for a red corpuscle to traverse the liver was only a fraction of the time taken to traverse the spleen. Also, applying the carbon monoxide technique, they showed that blood cells taken from the liver exhibited a saturation level at given time intervals no different from blood cells obtained elsewhere in the body—except the spleen where sequestered red corpuscles were protected for long periods.

The observations of Knisely (1939) and of Wakim and Mann (1942) remain to be explained, for the concept of intermittent activity of sinusoids and lobules depends largely on their work. Their concepts, indeed, are not borne out by any cytochemical or histological picture that has been reported (Wilson, 1958). Moreover, Maegraith (1958), reporting on transillumination studies, claims that intermittent flow was only seen exceptionally. The transillumination studies of Knisely (1939) and of Wakim and Mann

(1942) were confined to the edge of the liver, a vascular territory which may not be typical of the liver as a whole and it may be that the better perfused hilar regions do not show the same inter-mittency.

Although there may well be variations between species the con-cept of the hepato-portal system as a labile "capacity" rather than a labile store seems to be more acceptable on present evidence.

EFFECT OF ANAESTHESIA ON LIVER BLOOD FLOW AND METABOLISM

The effects of anaesthesia on liver blood flow and metabolism are controversial. Shackman, Graber and Melrose (1953) measured liver blood flow in man by bromsulphalein and found that with pentobarbitone anaesthesia there was a 30 per cent drop in liver blood flow and a 34 per cent drop in splanchnic oxygen consump-tion. Fisher, Russ, Selker and Fedor (1956) measured liver blood flow in the dog with bromsulphalein and found that pentobarbitone sodium did not affect flow, but ether anaesthesia increased flow from 49 ml./kg/min to 70 ml./kg/min. They did not report on oxygen consumption. Evringham, Brenneman and Horvath (1959) could similarly find no effect of sodium pentobarbitone anaesthesia on liver blood flow in dogs, measured by bromsulphalein, or on oxygen consumption. Birnie and Grayson (1952) found a transient fall in liver blood flow in the rat with ether anaesthesia and Grayson and Mendel (1956) found a reduction in liver temperature in the rat following pentobarbitone sodium anaesthesia, which was inter-preted as metabolic inhibition. It would seem that pentobarbitone sodium in both rat and man produces a prolonged metabolic de-pression in the liver. The effect on blood flow is probably short-lived and may be related more to changes in blood pressure than to metabolism.

EFFECT OF POSTURE ON SPLANCHNIC BLOOD FLOW

It has long been recognized that falls in blood pressure associated with changing from the horizontal to the vertical position are associated with accumulation of blood in the splanchnic area and subsequent vasoconstriction. Hill (1895) was of the opinion that the intestine was the main site of temporary pooling. It was clearly shown by Edholm (1942) that in the eviscerated cat, the blood pressure still fell when the animal was held in the upright position, but that the vascular compensation under these circumstances was diminished. Removal of the liver, however, completely abolished the fall in blood pressure with change in posture. It was concluded that the fall in blood pressure was mainly due to accumulation of blood in the liver, and that the intestines were partly responsible for compensation. The effect of posture on liver blood flow in man has been investigated by Culbertson, Wilkins, Inglefinger and Bradley (1951), using the bromsulphalein clearance technique. Liver blood flow, on tilting 75° from the horizontal to the near vertical position, fell from average initial levels of 995 ml./min/sq M to 620 ml./min/sq M. Blood pressure fell only 1 mm Hg for the group of six subjects. Calculated splanchnic resistance rose from 3·8 to 5·5 units. Wilkins, Culbertson and Inglefinger (1951) made similar measurements on hypertensive patients following splanchnic sympathectomy. Liver blood flow fell on tilting from 845 ml./min/sq M to 620 ml./min/sq M, and blood pressure fell from 149 mm Hg to 125 mm Hg. There was no change in splanchnic resistance. Although measurement of total liver blood flow and resistance gives no clue as to the site of resistance (intestine, liver), it was concluded that in man there is a sympathetically mediated increase in splanchnic resistance when the posture changes from the supine to the near vertical and that these changes in resistance are important in maintaining the arterial blood pressure.

Effect of exercise on splanchnic blood flow

The first observations of the effect of exercise on the splanchnic circulation were those of Barcroft and Florey (1929). They exteriorized in a dog the spleen and a patch of colonic mucosa. When the dog was exercised the spleen constricted and remained so. The colonic mucosa on the other hand became pale for about 20 seconds and then became red. Herrick, Grindley, Baldes and Mann (1940) measured superior mesenteric artery flow in conscious dogs with the thermostromuhr. In 17 experiments on exercise using three dogs, there was no change in superior mesenteric artery flow in six, an increase of 16–45 per cent in ten, and a fall of 14 per cent in one. After exercise there was a fall in flow of about 14 per cent. They concluded that although vasoconstriction may occur in the mesenteric arteries in exercise the changes in blood pressure overcame the reduction in flow. Wade *et al* (1956) have made a detailed study of the effect of leg exercise on liver blood flow and splanchnic blood volume in man. Liver blood flow was measured by the bromsulphalein technique and splanchnic blood volume with I^{131} labelled human serum albumin. In five normal subjects, splanchnic blood flow fell by a mean of 355 ml./min or by 19 per cent of the initial flow. Splanchnic blood volume fell by a mean of 400 ml. or 35 per cent of the initial volume. Splanchnic oxygen consumption fell from 20–34 per cent of the total oxygen uptake to 7–11 per cent of the total oxygen uptake.

It would seem that the splanchnic circulation can donate a considerable quantity of blood to the general circulation in exercise, presumably by constriction of the venous bed by mechanisms indicated by Alexander (1954).

HEPATIC BLOOD FLOW AND HEPATIC FUNCTION

Surprisingly little is known concerning the relation of hepatic blood flow to hepatic function.

In a study of hepatic blood flow distribution and hepatic function, Brauer (1958) confined himself to one aspect only of liver function, namely, the transfer of test substance—in this case chromium phosphate—from blood to liver cells. He was able to demonstrate that the transfer rate depended on many factors. One was blood concentration, another was temperature. But he was also able to show a direct correlation between transfer rate and blood flow. The relation was curvilinear and above an optimum perfusion rate the uptake was not significantly increased.

Experiments in which intrahepatic distribution rather than total flow was altered produced interesting results. Thus, adrenaline infusions had a most marked effect in lowering the efficiency of extraction—an effect bigger than could be explained merely on the basis of lowered blood flow.

These findings were similar to the findings of Andrews, Maegraith and Richards (1956), who, using bromsulphalein as their test substances, showed similar correlations but who also showed that bromsulphalein extraction was much more an affair of the hepatic arterial bed than of the portal. They claimed that bromsulphalein reaching the liver by the portal vein was largely stored, that reaching it by the hepatic arterial route was largely eliminated. This is in accord with Brauer's findings reported above since adrenaline has been shown to exert its main effect on the arterial supply to the liver, and if extraction depends so largely on the arterial as opposed to the portal venous bed, then adrenaline might be expected to reduce chromium phosphate extraction in the way described.

These observations are curious. They are difficult to link with present knowledge concerning the microanatomy of the hepatic circulation. Nevertheless, Andrews (1958) has suggested that bromsulphalein excretion (and probably also chromium phosphate extraction) may be performed by the bile ducts or, alternatively, by special parenchymal cells having a predominantly arterial supply.

These results apply to the effect of blood flow on local function. From the opposite viewpoint there appears to be little evidence suggesting that liver blood flow or blood distribution can be controlled directly by local functional considerations.

A limited knowledge is available concerning liver blood flow and its relation to metabolic functions of the liver.

Barcroft and Shore (1912) found a two-fold increase in hepatic artery flow in the fed animal as compared with the fasting. Bearn *et al.* (1952), using the bromsulphalein method for estimation of liver blood flow in man, showed that insulin hypoglycaemia produced a slight fall in splanchnic vascular resistance. In a further investigation, mainly directed to a study of hepatic glucose output, Billington, Paton, Reynolds and Sherlock (1954) claimed that the simultaneous administration of hexamethonium bromide in full ganglion-blocking doses prevented this fall in splanchnic vascular resistance during insulin hypoglycaemia.

Grayson and Kinnear (1958), in the rat and baboon, confirmed the drop in hepatic vascular resistance accompanying insulin hypoglycaemia (Fig. 7.9). They were not able to confirm that nervous factors or adrenaline were involved. Their findings in man (Grayson and Kinnear, 1962) were in many ways similar, although perhaps not so well marked. Insulin administration produced usually an augmentation in flow and a fall in hepatic resistance with a concomitant increase in local heat production (see appendix). Evidence was adduced suggesting that the effect on heat production was not secondary to the hypoglycaemia but a direct action of insulin. About 30 min (the actual time varies considerably) after the injection of insulin, a marked depression occurred in heat production which just preceded the onset of sweating and the other signs of marked hypoglycaemia. It is of interest that these marked

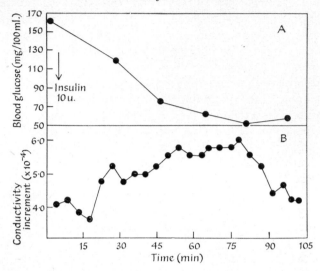

FIG. 7.9. The effect of intravenous insulin (10 i.u.) (A) on blood glucose, and (B) on liver blood flow (conductivity increment) in the anaesthetized baboon.

(Grayson and Kinnear, 1958.)

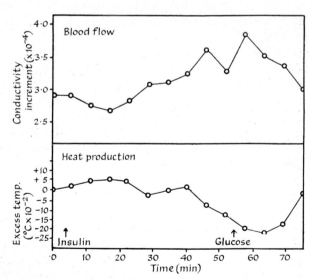

FIG. 7.10. The effect of insulin on blood flow (conductivity increment) and heat production in human liver.

(Grayson and Kinnear, 1962.)

depressions of metabolic heat production were not accompanied by any noticeable change in blood flow; indeed, in a number of experiments (Fig. 7.10) where the blood flow was already rising, it continued to rise during the period of metabolic inhibition.

Grayson and Kinnear (1962) also reported in man that intravenous injections of glucose produced increments of liver flow of up to 85 per cent (though usually less), which were rapid, brief in duration and usually accompanied by small decrements in heat pro-

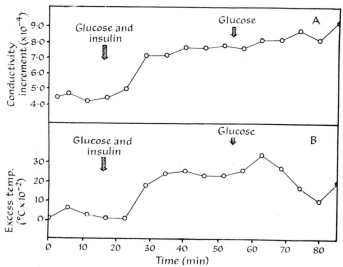

Fig. 7.11. Effect of glucose and insulin on heat production and blood flow in human liver. (A) liver blood flow (conductivity increment); (B) heat production.

(Grayson and Kinnear, 1962.)

duction. Combinations of insulin with glucose produced even more marked changes which were usually long lasting, peak changes being reached between one and two hours. In these experiments heat production was markedly raised (Fig. 7.11).

It is possible that these results may be related to the observations of Herrick, Mann, Essex and Baldes (1934) and Brandt, Castleman, Greenwald and Kelly (1954) that increases in splanchnic blood flow and oxygen consumption occur after feeding. Myers and Hickam (1948) find, however, that the splanchnic flow is unchanged and that the increased demand for oxygen is obtained by an increase in oxygen extraction.

Shoemaker, Itallie and Walker (1959) determined the effect of glucagon on hepatic blood flow and glucose output in conscious dogs. Blood flow was measured by the bromsulphalein method. Samples of portal venous blood were obtained from an indwelling catheter in the splenic vein. Glucagon, 0·4 mg caused a rise in hepatic venous glucose and a rise in hepatic blood flow of from 41 to 204 per cent. They suggest that the increased blood flow was a response to glycogenolysis. It is clear that heat production or oxygen consumption alone cannot be correlated with blood flow. Yet food ingestion or glucose or insulin or—most marked of all—glucose combined with insulin, have marked effects on blood flow. The nature of the mechanisms involved is at present elusive but it is clearly a problem of considerable importance the elucidation of which must await further work.

VIII

INTRAHEPATIC VASCULAR RELATIONSHIPS

ANY study of intrahepatic vascular relationships must take full account not merely of physiological findings but also of morphological evidence. Wilson (1958) has said, ". . . the lack of morphological evidence for the existence of the various control mechanisms can only be a source of humility for the morphologist". This may well be true, there remains nevertheless a remarkable complexity of anatomical structures to be considered. Brauer (1958) has summarized the situation succinctly: ". . . a variety of structural provisions capable of altering blood flow distribution in the liver have been reported: Sphincters—both pre and post sinusoidal (Knisely, Harding and Debacker, 1957); contractile tissue along certain portions of the vascular bed (Irwin and Macdonald, 1953); shunts bridging the sinusoidal bed, inferred from microsphere experiments (Prinzmetal *et al.*, 1948); in reference to the hepatic arterial supply in particular, the complex vascular plexuses surrounding the bile ducts (Andrews, Maegraith and Wenyon, 1949). Supplementing these is recent evidence indicating chromaffin tissue in the sinusoids themselves (Adams-Ray and Nordenstam, 1958); an observation which opens up interesting possibilities of local control in the liver."

THE STABILITY OF LIVER BLOOD FLOW

Bradley *et al.* (1945) found liver blood flow in man to be stable. Grayson and Ginsburg (1954), on the basis of observations made on conscious and unconscious rats and rabbits, stated that blood flow in the liver was remarkably constant and showed no trace of the sort of spontaneous fluctuations observed in skin and bowel.

These findings were not in accord with the observations of Knisely (1939) and of Wakim and Mann (1942), who from direct observations of sinusoidal activity at the edge of the liver, found fluctuating sinusoidal activity and that 78 per cent of sinusoids were inactive at any one time. Daniel and Pritchard (1951a) injected thorotrast into a tributary of the superior mesenteric vein, and made rapid serial angiograms of the liver, in rats, cats, guinea pigs and goats. The contrast medium showed, in succession, the portal tree, a diffuse shadow within the liver representing the filled sinusoids, and finally, outflow through the hepatic veins into the inferior vena cava. Two types of picture were obtained (Fig. 8.1). In the first

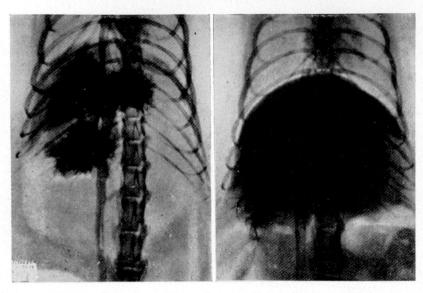

FIG. 8.1. Normal rats. Figure shows angiograms from two different rats taken at same time intervals after injection of thorotrast into small tributaries of the superior mesenteric veins. To illustrate different patterns of filling. Both figures show the sinusoidal stage of portal venous circulation. Right-hand figure—sinuses at periphery well filled. Left-hand figure—sinusoids at the periphery not filled.

(Daniel and Pritchard, 1951*a*.)

type the portal blood flow was evenly distributed throughout the liver, the filling of sinusoids being so complete that the liver margins were clearly defined. In the second type, there was a patchy sinusoidal filling confined to the central portion of the liver. The reason for the differences was not clear. Either picture could be obtained in "normal" animals and the restricted circulation could not be produced by nerve stimulation. Transillumination observations are micro-observations referring only to the edge of the exposed liver. They are not strictly comparable with observations made on whole liver or large volumes of liver and random fluctuations observed at capillary level may be perfectly compatible with a steady total liver blood flow. The observations of Daniel and Pritchard are harder to reconcile with the concept of the steady state. It is also possible that the stability reported by Grayson and Ginsburg (1954) was due to the fact that they were recording from small portions of the liver in the deeper parts which even according to Daniel and Pritchard demonstrate vascular filling at all times.

Graf and Rosell (1958), using a heated thermocouple technique, have reported the occasional occurrence of large, apparently spontaneous fluctuations in liver blood flow in human subjects. However, these changes, which were not unlike those reported by Grayson (1951) with reference to the bowel mucosa, were usually linked to the position of the body, to pain, or to emotional factors.

Grayson and Kinnear (1962), also using a heated thermocouple, confirmed the findings of Graf and Rosell with respect to rhythmic variations of flow in man. These occurred in most subjects although the frequency and amplitude varied. The amplitude of the fluctuations was never more than ±10 per cent change around the mean. The frequency was usually of the order of one cycle complete in 10–15 min. These workers could find no basis for this rhythm. It was not related to respiration. It was observed when the subject was in a hot, humid environment (80°F; R.H. 98 per cent) or in a cooler, drier environment (70°F; R.H. 60 per cent); it did not seem to be linked to any change in environment. According to Graf *et al.* (1958) the rhythm was abolished by anaesthesia and some narcotic drugs.

VASCULAR SHUNTS WITHIN THE LIVER

At various times the possibility of a number of arterio-venous communications within the liver has been postulated. There is evidence that there are direct communications between the portal vein and hepatic veins in the liver. Prinzmetal, Ornitz, Simpkin and Bergman (1948) injected glass microspheres into the portal circulation of dogs and recovered spheres of up to 180 μ in diameter from the hepatic veins, a size of sphere too large to pass through the sinusoidal bed. Their work gave no indication of the exact site of the anastomoses. A second type of portal hepatic vein communication has been described by Daniel and Pritchard (1951a). They injected the venous tree of the liver of the cat with colloidal silver iodide and from radiomicrographs demonstrated that major branches of the portal vein and hepatic vein run parallel to each other and have interdigitating twigs which are separated from one another by very short lengths of sinusoid. They suggested that this was a pathway through which blood can flow from a major portal vessel to a major hepatic vein without passing through the peripheral sinusoids. In support of this idea is their observation that when they observed the pattern of restricted circulation in their angiograms, thorotrast rapidly appeared in the inferior vena cava, indicating a shorter transit time for dye in the liver.

Andrews *et al.* (1956) adduced evidence suggesting the possible existence of hepatic artery–hepatic venous shunts. They showed that acetylcholine constricted the hepatic veins of dog and monkey and made the interesting observation that the vasoconstrictor effect was greater when the acetylcholine was injected into the hepatic artery than into the portal vein. In the dog the effect was 5–20 times greater; in the monkey up to 100 times greater. They concluded that some, at least, of the arterial blood by-passed the sinusoids.

There is also evidence of the existence of shunts linking the hepatic artery and portal vein. The anatomical evidence has already been referred to in a previous chapter. Grayson, Ginsburg and Walker (1954 unpublished) measured portal pressure by cannulating the splenic vein in the rat. On clamping the portal inflow on the bowel side of the vein they found that in about 50 per cent of the experiments portal pressure declined rapidly; in the remainder there was, however, a rise in portal pressure which in some experiments reached levels of 200 mm saline or higher. This they regarded as evidence of free communication between the hepatic arterial radicles and the portal venous radicles (it was thought unlikely that pressure of this magnitude could be transmitted directly through the sinusoids). There is also evidence that these communications may be patent in cirrhosis of the liver. Longmire, Mulder, Mahoney and Methinkoff (1958) injected serum albumin labelled with I[131] into the hepatic artery and found radioactivity in the portal vein. None of this work helps in interpreting function but it does suggest that under some circumstances patent hepatic arterial–portal venous communication may be a factor in portal hypertension.

THE RELATIVE CONTRIBUTION OF HEPATIC ARTERY AND PORTAL VEIN TO LIVER BLOOD FLOW

One of the difficulties in determining the relative contribution of the hepatic artery and portal vein to liver blood flow is that occlusion of the hepatic artery may lead to alteration in the portal contribution and occlusion of the portal vein might similarly lead to alteration in the hepatic artery contribution (Schweigk, 1922). This was certainly found in the experiments of Macleod and Pearce (1914), who found in one experiment that liver outflow fell from 585 ml./min to 392 ml./min after hepatic artery ligation and then rose to 445 ml./min. Ginsburg and Grayson (1954) measured liver blood flow in the rat by internal calorimetry and showed that when

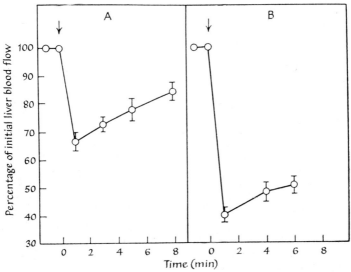

FIG. 8.2. The effect on liver blood flow (conductivity increment) of occlusion (A) of the coeliac artery, and (B) of the portal circulation. The ranges shown indicate the standard errors of the means observed in eight and six rats respectively.

(Ginsburg and Grayson, 1954.)

the coeliac artery was ligated, there was a sudden drop in flow to 65 per cent of the initial level followed by recovery to 80 per cent of initial levels (Fig. 8.2 A). Occlusion of the portal vein resulted in a drop in flow to 40 per cent of initial levels followed by recovery to 50 per cent (Fig. 8.2 B). On the other hand, Green *et al.* (1959) failed to find a change in hepatic artery flow when the portal vein was occluded or in the portal vein flow when the hepatic artery was occluded. They noted, however, that in experiments where portal vein flow was measured by an electromagnetic flowmeter involving cannulation, hepatic artery flow was 147 ml./min compared with 85·8 ml./min in animals without portal vein cannulation.

Values obtained by different techniques are shown in Table 8.1. Apart from the wide range of values reported by Soskin *et al.* (1938) and Grindlay *et al.* (1941) reports of hepatic artery contribution to total liver blood flow vary between 20 and 40 per cent.

TABLE 8.1

Hepatic artery contribution to liver blood flow

Author	*Method*	*% arterial contribution*	
Burton-Opitz (1910)	Stromuhr	24–44	Dog
Macleod & Pearce (1914)	Outflow collection	30	Dog
Blalock & Mason (1936)	Outflow collection	19·5	Dog
Grab *et al.* (1929)	Thermostromuhr	19	Dog
Grindlay *et al.* (1941)	Thermostromuhr	10–80	Dog
Soskin *et al.* (1938)	Thermostromuhr	10–90	Dog
Scweigk (1932)	Thermostromuhr	20–25	Dog
Green *et al.* (1959)	Electromagnetic flowmeter	30	Dog
Barcroft & Shore (1912)	Outflow collection	34	Cat
Ginsburg & Grayson (1954)	Internal calorimetry	35	Rat

Effect of varying blood pressure on the hepatic artery contribution

Grayson and Mendel (1957*a*) determined the contribution of the hepatic artery to liver blood flow at different blood pressure levels. Liver blood flow in the rat was determined by internal calorimetry, and blood pressure was controlled by allowing the animal to bleed into or receive blood from a reservoir held at a suitable pressure. The contribution of hepatic artery flow was determined by occluding the artery at different blood pressure levels and determining the effect on liver blood flow. Similar observations were made for the spleen. The results are summarized in Fig. 8.3. At blood pressure levels of 120 mm Hg the hepatic arterial contribution was 30 per cent and at 80 mm Hg it was 70 per cent. As the blood pressure was lowered further the percentage contribution of the hepatic artery began to decline. At pressures of 20 mm Hg, there was no detectable flow through the artery. Resistance to hepatic artery flow calculated in arbitrary units as perfusion pressure/flow (conductivity increment), fell with declining pressure and then increased to high values as the blood pressure fell further. It was suggested that "critical closure" occurred in the hepatic artery radicles at a pressure of 20 mm Hg. The portal venous reactions were different. The portal contribution fell with fall in blood pressure (Fig. 8.3) but at very low blood pressure levels it was still contributing to liver blood flow. The resistance to portal flow, calculated from portal pressure and flow (conductivity increment) after hepatic artery occlusion at the various blood pressure levels, showed a rise as the blood pressure was lowered to 80 mm Hg, and then a progressive fall. There was no clear evidence of critical closure.

The observation that the hepatic artery contribution to liver blood flow increases as the blood pressure falls has been confirmed in the dog by Fischer, Takacs and Molnar (1958), who measured

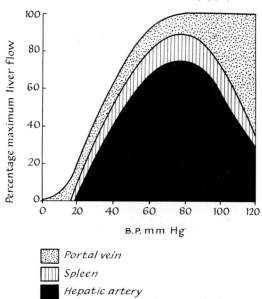

Portal vein

Spleen

Hepatic artery

FIG. 8.3. The percentage contributions to liver blood flow at different blood pressure levels of the portal vein, hepatic artery and spleen.
(Data derived from Grayson and Mendel, 1957a.)

Note increased percentage contribution of hepatic artery and spleen at systemic arterial pressures of 80 mm Hg. Note also no detectable hepatic arterial or splenic contributions below arterial pressures of 18 to 20 mm Hg (critical closure).

hepatic artery flow with a rotameter and total liver blood flow by the bromsulphalein technique. They found that the hepatic artery could contribute 60 per cent of the total liver blood flow when the blood pressure fell by 80 mm Hg.

AUTOREGULATION OF LIVER BLOOD FLOW

Johnson (1953), using the technique of "internal calorimetry", demonstrated a phenomenon suggestive of autoregulation of liver blood flow. He showed that on lowering the blood pressure over the

range 140–80 mm Hg in the rat liver, blood flow remained constant
(with each pressure drop there was a transient vasoconstrictor epi-
sode, followed rapidly by a return to pre-bleeding levels). On
lowering the pressure below 80 mm Hg the blood flow declined.

Ginsburg and Grayson (1954) further investigated the phenomenon. They showed that it was not affected by coeliac neurectomy, by ganglion blockade, by atropine, or by adrenalectomy.

At first glance, therefore, the phenomenon had much in common
with autoregulation. They avoided the use of this word, however,
since the response did not appear to be strictly "auto". They could

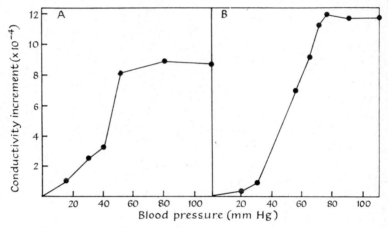

Fig. 8.4. Liver blood flow (conductivity increment) responses to
changing arterial blood pressure. Liver blood supply intact. (A) rat;
(B) baboon. Note "autoregulatory" type of curve.

(Grayson and Mendel, 1957a.)

not demonstrate it in livers perfused through the portal vein; they
could not demonstrate it after ligation of the hepatic artery; the
response was greatly modified by splenectomy; it could not be
demonstrated in severely shocked animals and could occasionally
be abolished by deep anaesthesia. Although it was clear that the
liver vasculature was deeply involved it was felt that the word
"autoregulation" could only really be applied to tissues which exhibited this type of regulation when isolated and perfused. Accordingly Ginsburg and Grayson adopted a compromise description
and referred to their findings as "intrinsic regulation" of liver blood
flow.

The reactions of total liver blood flow to mean systemic arterial
pressure are illustrated in Fig. 8.4. This raises the question as to

whether autoregulation might occur elsewhere in the splanchnic area. That autoregulation might occur in the branches of the mesenteric artery has been suggested by Johnson (1960) and by Texter, Merril, Schwartz, Vandersteppen and Haddy (1962). Johnson perfused the isolated terminal ileum of the dog and found a decrease in resistance on lowering the blood pressure (Fig. 8.5). The

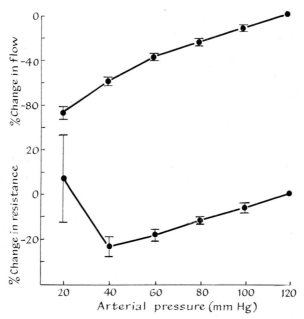

FIG. 8.5. Perfused dog intestine—showing changes in blood flow and resistance with differing arterial perfusion pressures.
(Johnson, 1960.)

result was obtained in 72 per cent of perfusions and was best seen in the fresh preparation. The response was not due to a local reflex, changes in intestinal volume or changes in intestinal tone. Trapold (1956) and Selkurt *et al.* (1958), however, have failed to confirm these findings (Fig. 2.4).

Grayson and Mendel (1957a) measured liver blood flow in the rat by internal calorimetry. They ligated the hepatic artery and removed the spleen so that the sole source of blood supply to the liver was the gastro-intestinal tract. The blood pressure was lowered in steps and the effect on liver blood flow determined. In these experiments there was no autoregulation manifest in the gastro-intestinal outflow (Fig. 8.6). It may well be that the mesenteric arteries themselves would display autoregulation but that in the tissue as a whole, the effect is overridden by some other—possibly neurogenic—vasoconstrictor effect. Whatever the explanation of the apparent discrepancy, it is unlikely that intrinsic regulation of hepatic flow can be explained on the basis of mesenteric autoregulation.

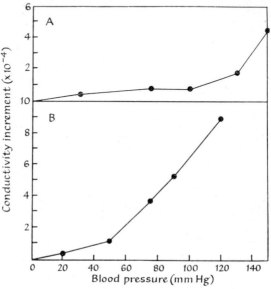

Fig. 8.6. Liver blood flow (conductivity increment) responses to changing arterial blood pressure (different rats). (A) 24 hours after ligation of hepatic artery; (B) 4 days after ligation of hepatic artery. In both cases splenectomy had been performed previously. Note different pattern of response to that shown in Fig. 8.4 with intact hepatic blood flow.

The relationship described, whereby the mean liver flow with its vessels intact remained constant in the face of varying perfusion pressure, would seem to derive from a property of the hepatic blood vessels. It was not seen in perfusion experiments where the liver was perfused through the portal vein (Grayson, 1954). In experiments where the sole source of supply to the liver was the hepatic artery the results were somewhat equivocal (Grayson and Mendel, 1957a). In some experiments the curve was autoregulatory in shape, in others it was not. Torrance (1961), however, has described pressure/flow curves for the hepatic artery of the dog in which there was a convexity toward the flow axis (Fig. 8.7), with critical

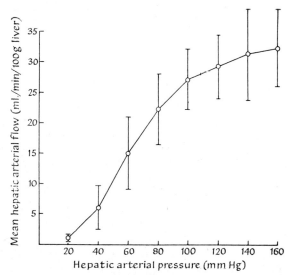

FIG. 8.7. The standardized pressure flow diagram of the hepatic arterial circulation in the dog. Vertical lines are standard errors for twenty-five experiments. Hepatic artery flow measured by a density flowmeter. Note "autoregulatory" type of curve.

(Torrance, 1961.)

closure at about 20 mm Hg. The shape of the curve was not affected by blockade with hexamethonium bromide.

IX

THE EFFECTS OF HAEMORRHAGE AND SHOCK ON THE SPLANCHNIC CIRCULATION

I T has long been recognized that a sudden severe loss of fluid leads to a widespread vasoconstriction affecting many structures, amongst others the gastro-intestinal tract and liver (Malcolm, 1910; Mann, 1915). The role of the gastro-intestinal and hepatic vessels in relation to baroreceptor responses has already been discussed. A sudden drop in blood pressure has been shown to produce reflex vasoconstriction in the splanchnic area. Nevertheless in prolonged hypotensive states a different role has been frequently ascribed to the splanchnic area. The phenomenon of "pooling" and the possible elaboration of vasodepressive substances by the liver in hypotensive states might be expected to have an effect on blood pressure control quite the reverse of reflex vasoconstriction. The question to be examined, therefore, is how far does the splanchnic area participate in blood pressure regulation via the baroreceptor mechanisms and how far does it play a detrimental role in prolonged hypotensive states. A number of studies have to be reported.

Gastro-intestinal tract

There is general agreement that a fall in blood pressure leads to a reduction of intestinal blood flow in all species reported on. The mechanism of the fall is, however, not so clear. There remains disagreement as to the relative importance of active vasoconstriction and the passive effects of reduced perfusion pressure.

Selkurt, Alexander and Patterson (1947) measured portal blood flow by a direct collection technique in splenectomized dogs. They found that when the blood pressure in an 8-kg dog was lowered from 140 mm Hg to 60 mm Hg, mesenteric blood flow fell from 26 ml./kg/min to 7·7 ml./kg/min with a gradual recovery to 9·0 ml./kg/min. Resistance to flow rose from 0·654 to 1·00 peripheral resistance units. Selkurt and Brecher (1956) measured intestinal blood flow during haemorrhage by means of a bubble flowmeter in the portal vein of dogs. Mesenteric blood flow fell from 309 ml./min to 127 ml./min when the blood pressure was 60 mm Hg.

There was, however, no significant change in mesenteric vascular resistance. Similarly, Levy (1958) found that blood loss to the extent of 20 ml./kg body weight in dogs lowered portal inflow by 39 per cent but resistance to mesenteric flow was unchanged. Friedman (1961) also failed to find an increase in mesenteric resistance in haemorrhage. Gregg (1962) measured the effect of haemorrhage on superior mesenteric artery flow with an implanted electromagnetic flowmeter in conscious dogs. A haemorrhage of 950 ml. lowered systemic blood pressure from 128 to 45 mm Hg, and mesenteric blood flow from 450 ml./min to 50 ml./min. Mesenteric vascular resistance increased by about three times. Sapirstein *et al.* (1960), using clearance of Rb[86] in the rat, reported that a haemorrhage of 10 ml./kg body weight lowered blood pressure from 121 to 90 mm Hg and intestinal flow from 8·5 to 4·9 ml./min. There was a 30 per cent increase in resistance. More severe haemorrhage (20 ml./kg body weight) lowered the blood pressure to 28 mm Hg, blood flow fell to 1·0 ml./min and vascular resistance doubled.

Interpretation of resistance changes of this kind are always difficult. In isolated tissues perfused with blood, resistance is now known to increase with decreasing perfusion pressure (except where autoregulation occurs). In most of the experiments quoted above there was, in fact, little or no change in resistance with declining perfusion pressure. This does not indicate, therefore, that the blood flow/blood pressure relations were merely passive, nor are the reported relationships really compatible with any major increase in vasomotor tone in the bowel. It could well be that such results really uphold Johnson's findings (1960) of autoregulation in the bowel. However, since in some experiments there was a rise in resistance as the blood pressure was lowered, the possibility of some increase in vasomotor activity with lowering of the blood pressure cannot be totally excluded. It is, indeed, possible that some of the variability in reported results may be the results of a conflict between the opposing effects of autoregulation and vasomotor tone.

It is worthy of note, too, that there is evidence of increased venomotor tone in the intestinal veins during haemorrhage. Thus, Alexander (1955) has shown from experiments on the distensibility of intestinal veins in dogs, that venomotor tone rises in haemorrhage and, since venomotor tone can be increased by baroreceptor reflexes it would seem that there is an active constriction of intestinal veins in haemorrhage.

Liver blood flow

Liver blood flow has been shown by a number of investigations to decrease during haemorrhage. Werner, MacCanon and Horvath (1952), using bromsulphalein to measure liver blood flow in dogs, found that a blood loss of 1 per cent of the body weight caused a 20 per cent reduction in liver blood flow and a fall in blood pressure of 20 mm Hg. Heinnemann, Smythe and Marks (1953) similarly found that haemorrhage of 1·3–3·9 per cent of the body weight produced falls in liver blood flow of 40 to 81 per cent but that normal levels were restored in 23–70 min. Hamrick and Myers (1955) bled dogs between 32 and 65 per cent of their blood volume to attain a blood pressure of 67 mm Hg. Liver blood flow fell from 47 to 18 ml./kg body weight/min. Reynell, Marks, Chidsey and Bradley (1955) found that in the dog bled to 50 mm Hg, a fall in hepatic blood flow of 40 per cent occurred associated with a slight increase in splanchnic resistance. Complete recovery of flow was observed in two hours although the blood pressure was kept at 50 mm Hg. Smythe (1959), using chromium phosphate clearance to measure hepatic flow, did not find a fall in blood flow with a blood loss of 25 ml./kg body weight in dogs, a result which he attributed to the presence of the spleen. Blood loss of 33 ml./kg body weight, however, caused a 50 per cent fall in liver blood flow with a blood pressure of 40 mm Hg. The only data relevant to man is that obtained by Bearn, Billing, Edholm and Sherlock (1951) in studies of hepatic blood flow during fainting. They measured liver blood flow by bromsulphalein clearance, and induced fainting by a combination of venous occlusion and haemorrhage. During the faint, blood pressure fell from 120 mm Hg to 45 mm Hg, and flow fell from 1,150–500 ml./min/sq M. During haemorrhage and immediately preceding the faint, there was an increase in splanchnic vascular resistance, but during the faint splanchnic vascular resistance fell and they considered that splanchnic vasodilatation had occurred. Ginsburg and Grayson (1954) reported that a rapid drop in blood pressure in the rat resulted in a fall in liver blood flow of short duration. This was partly passive and partly a sympathetically mediated reflex. In any case the intrinsic factors already referred to rapidly restored equilibrium levels of blood flow. There is, in fact, no real discrepancy between the findings of Ginsburg and Grayson and those of other workers referred to above since "intrinsic regulation" ceases to be effective at mean systemic pressures below

80 mm Hg and most of the experimental work on haemorrhage has dealt with blood pressure falls below this range.

It is, therefore, generally agreed that the effect of moderate to severe haemorrhage in most species is to produce an initial marked drop in liver blood flow although it has been noted by Heinemann *et al.* (1953), Johnson (1954) and Reynell *et al.* (1955) that blood flow tends to improve and vascular resistance to decrease as the blood pressure is maintained at low levels.

The effect of haemorrhage on hepatic vascular resistance has been shown by Selkurt and Brecher (1956) in the dog to be an increase in intrahepatic portal vein resistance, which rose three-fold with arterial blood pressures of 55–60 mm Hg. Hepatic artery flow fell from 175 to 100 ml./min and showed a recovery to 130 ml./min without significant change in resistance.

The splanchnic fraction of the cardiac output

It is clear that during haemorrhage a substantial reduction occurs in blood flow to the splanchnic area. Whether this reduction is of the magnitude one would expect from a major component of the peripheral resistance actively participating in compensatory baro-receptor responses is another matter. Indeed, there is evidence to suggest that the reduction in splanchnic blood flow is not so great as in other tissues. This is implied by some of the results already quoted which show some baroreceptor activity in the bowel, questionable baroreceptor activity in the liver and a total response to lowered blood pressure which is far from spectacular. There is even more direct evidence bearing on this point. Rous and Gilding (1929) reported that severe haemorrhage resulted in an almost complete deprivation of blood supply to the skin, skeletal muscle, omentum and bladder whereas the muscles of respiration, swallowing, the gut, liver and pancreas remained adequately supplied. Rein and Rossler (1929) pointed out that haemorrhage caused a much smaller percentage reduction in blood flow to the intestines than in the extremities. Blalock and Levy (1937) bled dogs to blood pressures of 80–100 mm Hg. Within 5–10 min, portal flow was reduced by 53 per cent compared with 76 per cent for the extremities. Werner *et al.* (1952) found the splanchnic fraction of the cardiac output, 32 per cent, unchanged in mild haemorrhage (1 per cent of body weight). Frank, Frank, Jacob, Weigal, Korman and Fine (1956) found that the splanchnic fraction of the cardiac output increased by about 3 per cent in severe haemorrhage in the dog.

Reynell *et al.* (1955) also noted that with haemorrhage in the dog, the splanchnic fraction of the cardiac output rose from 23·8 to 30·8 per cent when the blood pressure was 50 mm Hg and was unchanged from the controls when the blood pressure was 40 mm Hg. Sapirstein *et al.* (1960) reported an increase of 6 per cent in the splanchnic fraction of the cardiac output in rats with a haemorrhage of 10 ml./kg and a fall by 2 per cent with more severe haemorrhage (25 ml./kg). They concluded that "contrary to standard teaching, the splanchnic blood flow is not disproportionally curtailed in haemorrhage, despite the biological attractiveness of such a curtailment which has withstood observation to the contrary for more than 30 years". This conclusion is well supported in the literature.

Responses in the mesentery during haemorrhage

The mesentery has proved a more rewarding medium of investigation than the bowel itself. Its accessibility makes direct visual observation a relatively straightforward procedure.

It is, nevertheless, a complex structure. It carries the large and small branches of the arteries of supply to the bowel. It also carries the veins which drain the gut. Despite this it has a vascular individuality of its own. The possession of a profusion of arterio-venous anastomoses and of the metarterioles or central channels of Chambers and Zweifach (1944) means that its venous drainage cannot simply be regarded as the venous drainage of the bowel. Nor can all the blood flowing along the mesenteric arterial branches be regarded as simply destined to supply the bowel. The complexity of its vascular architecture means, indeed, that from a circulatory point of view the mesentery must be regarded as an important vascular tissue in its own right, a potential storehouse of blood and an important site of blood flow regulation.

Page and Abell (1943) observed the reactions of the larger vessels of the rat mesentery following repeated removal of blood from the femoral vein. They reported that over a period of some hours there was a progressive narrowing of the arteries and veins persisting until just before death when relaxation of the arteries occurred accompanied by a precipitous fall in blood pressure. The vasoconstriction they showed to be largely dependent on the integrity of the nerve supply to the part.

A more extensive study of the problem was undertaken by Zweifach, Lowenstein and Chambers (1944), using in the first place the meso-appendix of the rat and, later, the mesentery of the dog. They

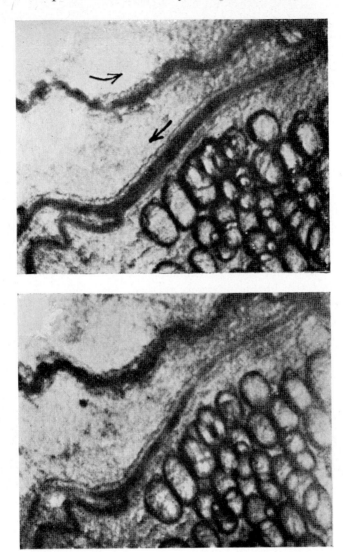

FIG. 9.1. Reaction of vessels of the rat meso-appendix to acute haemorrhage (stills from microcinematograph). Effect of moderate blood loss (4 per cent body weight). Upper figure—before bleeding. Upper arrow on non-muscular venule, lower arrow on arteriole—this branches to left, lower branch—metarteriole. Lower figure after bleeding showing partial constriction of arteriole, congestion of venule and metarteriole not affected.

(Zweifach, Lowenstein and Chambers, 1944.)

showed that removal of blood to the extent of 1 per cent of the total body weight had no effect either on the skin or on the mesentery. Bleeding to 2 per cent of the body weight produced marked ischaemia in the skin and some restriction of blood flow in the mesenteric capillaries though no change occurred in the larger vessels. A further bleed to the total extent of 4 per cent of the body weight, however, had marked effects and was accompanied by a significant mortality. Mesenteric arteries constricted to half their initial calibre and as the blood pressure fell to 50 to 60 mm Hg there was a marked slowing of the capillary flow. Increased vasomotion with prolongation of the vasoconstrictor phase occurred and the flow was restricted to the central channels (metarterioles) (Fig. 9.1). The effect was to reduce, almost to zero, the amount of blood passing through the capillary bed, and the main channel whereby blood passed from arteriole to venule appeared to be through simple, direct arterio-venous anastomoses. With more extreme bleeds, the animal was unable to maintain even a low blood pressure, and in the mesentery stagnation of blood occurred, involving more and more capillaries. There was distension at the venous end of the capillaries which caused mechanical obstruction to flow in the small veins and was regarded as a further factor in causing "pooling" of blood in the mesentery.

It will be apparent that these findings have many points in common with what has already been described with reference to the bowel. In the first place it is clear that the mesentery is less responsive to acute falls in blood pressure than, for example, the skin. In the second place, when it does respond, it does so by a process of vasoconstriction. An interesting point, however, is that owing to the peculiar configuration of the mesenteric circulation, one result of this response is a build-up of venous pressure and a damming-back of blood in the micro-vessels.

THE SPLANCHNIC CIRCULATION IN PROLONGED HYPOTENSION AND OLIGAEMIC SHOCK

The use of the term "shock" to describe the terminal stages of cardio-vascular collapse which ensue on a number of extreme stress situations is perhaps unfortunate. It is, however, hallowed by usage and, in any case, it might be difficult to suggest anything better.

In this work we are concerned in the main with oligaemic shock, a phrase we shall use to describe the terminal phases of exposure to sustained haemorrhagic hypotension. It may perhaps be most readily defined by reference to a relatively simple experimental situation in which an animal is allowed to bleed into a closed system against a pressure of about 35 mm Hg. At first blood is lost rapidly into the reservoir; the rate of blood loss then slows until bleeding has stopped altogether. Up to this moment, it is possible to produce recovery by transfusion of the shed blood. After this stage, which may take several hours to reach, blood begins to retransfuse spontaneously and before long, death supervenes. It is this last stage of spontaneous transfusion, where no amount of blood transfusion will produce more than a transient amelioration of blood pressure, that is designated shock.

The changes in the splanchnic circulation during profound hypotension and oligaemic shock so produced have been extensively investigated, in order to define the nature of the resistance changes in prolonged hypotension, the effect of retransfusion and the vascular changes in the terminal state.

Intestinal circulation

Selkurt *et al.* (1947) found that during prolonged hypotension two types of response occurred in the intestinal circulation. In some dogs, mesenteric resistance increased in the hypotensive period, and on transfusion with blood fell temporarily to below average levels and finally returned to normal levels. These animals tended to survive. In others, mesenteric resistance declined continuously through the hypotensive period, portal pressure was elevated and arterial pressure tended to decline. These animals tended to die fulminantly. Selkurt *et al.* concluded that in these animals, the raised portal pressure and low arterial perfusion pressure favoured pooling of blood and contributed to the irreversibility of shock. Selkurt and Brecher (1956), using bristle flowmeters to measure portal flow, found little change in mesenteric resistance in the hypotensive period but found that mesenteric resistance decreased as a terminal event. Johnson and Selkurt (1958) used the weight of a loop of bowel as an index of vascularity. During prolonged hypotension there was a fall in weight of the segment suggesting a constriction of vessels. In the late stages there was usually a small rise in weight which on retransfusion of blood rose to higher levels than the controls (Fig. 9.2). These results were taken as indicating a reduction in resistance and pooling of blood. Friedman (1961) measured intestinal resistance and plasma volume in

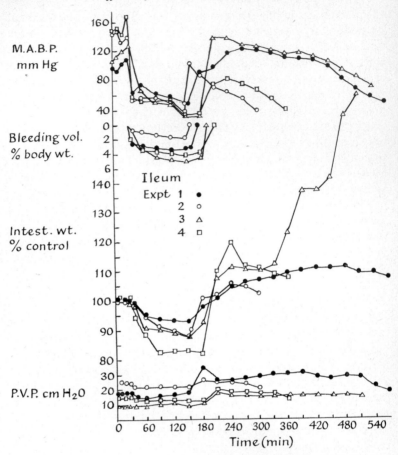

FIG. 9.2. Intestinal weight changes in "shock". Experiments on four dogs. M.A.B.P.—mean arterial blood pressure. P.V.P.—portal venous pressure. Showing initial diminutions in weight followed by variable increments.

(Johnson and Selkurt, 1958.)

the dog with prolonged hypotension. The mesenteric artery was perfused from the carotid artery to allow flow measurements. Two types of response were seen. In 10 out of 21 experiments there was no change in mesenteric vascular resistance either during the hypotensive period or on retransfusion, but mesenteric plasma volume was reduced by 25 per cent. In the second group, there was again no change in mesenteric vascular resistance during the hypotensive period, but on retransfusion mesenteric vascular resistance increased to 120 per cent above the control values and plasma volume fell by 65 per cent. The percentage reduction in splanchnic volume for both groups was greater than the percentage change in blood volume and Friedman considered that the splanchnic circulation contributed blood to the systemic circulation in shock. In the conscious dog, Gregg (1962) found that the increase in resistance in the mesenteric bed which occurred soon after haemorrhage persisted during the period of prolonged hypotension and on retransfusion. There was no evidence of "a reduction of arteriolar resistance" in the bowel in shock. Alexander (1955) has shown that although venoconstriction occurs in the mesenteric veins immediately after haemorrhage, prolonged hypotension results in a loss of venomotor tone and dilatation of veins. If blood was reinfused venous tone was returned to normal, but in severe shock the veins remain dilated. He considered the venomotor mechanism important in allowing pooling of blood in the venous bed.

Liver blood flow in prolonged haemorrhage and shock

There is evidence, during prolonged haemorrhage, of a rise in intrahepatic resistance to portal flow, which is followed by a decrease in resistance as shock supervenes. Wiggers, Opdyke and Johnson (1946) showed in the dog, a progressive increase in intrahepatic resistance during sustained hypotension which was associated with a rise in portal pressure. They claimed that resistance to portal flow increased relatively more than resistance to mesenteric outflow, a condition which favoured pooling of blood in the intestine. Friedman, Frank and Fine (1951) accounted for the increased resistance to portal flow which they found in the dog, on the basis of constriction of intrahepatic veins, which persisted after retransfusion and which they considered was due to sympathetic activity. Johnson (1954) obtained similar results in the rat exposed to prolonged hypotension. Neurogenic considerations could only account for the initial effects and the progressive increase in vascular resistance which occurred, and persisted after retransfusion, was independent of sympathetic activity. He found further that the increase in resistance to portal flow was not dependent upon the hepatic artery, since it occurred after hepatic artery ligation. When the sole source of blood to the liver was the hepatic artery, there was no increase in resistance in prolonged hypotension. He suggested that the increase in resistance to portal flow in hypotension may have arisen from contraction of the sinusoids themselves. Cull,

Scibetta and Selkurt (1956) compared resistance changes in the mesenteric artery and hepatic artery in prolonged hypotension in the dog. They confirmed the rise in portal pressure but noted that in this species both the hepatic artery and mesenteric artery resistance increased, the changes in resistance in the hepatic artery being the greater. On retransfusion, mesenteric resistance fell, and portal venous pressure increased further, which they attributed to increased mesenteric flow with maintained intrahepatic resistance. Hepatic artery resistance fell slowly, but when peak hepatic artery flow occurred, mesenteric artery resistance again increased, which they considered evidence for reciprocity of hepatic artery and mesenteric artery (and indirectly portal venous) flow. Selkurt and Brecher (1960) similarly found in the dog an increased intrahepatic resistance to portal flow, which increased on retransfusion and fell as a terminal event during shock.

It would seem that in prolonged hypotension in the dog, increase in hepatic resistance to portal flow is consistently found, while resistance to flow in the mesenteric bed is only slightly increased. When the stage of irreversibility is reached, mesenteric resistance shows little change but intrahepatic resistance may fall. There is no evidence of a profound vascular collapse in the splanchnic bed.

The dog has been used extensively for the study of shock. It must be borne in mind that the dog has unusual anatomical features, both in the extensive vascularity of the intestine and in having a definite sphincter mechanism in the hepatic veins. Selkurt and Rothe (1962) have recently compared the responses to prolonged hypotension in the dog with those obtained in the squirrel monkey. Portal flow was measured with an electronically timed bubble flowmeter. During hypotension a rise in intrahepatic resistance was again recorded, but not nearly so marked as in the dog. Resistance to mesenteric flow increased slightly and then returned to initial levels. On retransfusion, intrahepatic resistance returned to normal and portal pressure fell (in contrast to the dog where portal pressure increased on retransfusion). Terminal events were a rise in intrahepatic resistance and a slight fall in mesenteric resistance. It would seem then that part of the persistent increase in intrahepatic resistance in the dog is associated with the presence of hepatic sphincters. Unfortunately the monkey has extensive portal-caval anastomoses (Child, 1954) which may have affected the pattern of portal pressure in these experiments.

Circulation in bowel wall and mesentery in prolonged hypotension

One of the most detailed studies of prolonged hypotension was that of Zweifach, Lee, Hyman and Chambers (1944), who studied the changes occurring in the omentum of the dog in response to exposure to periods of hypotension lasting 2 to $2\frac{1}{2}$ hours.

The initial reactions were as described previously in this chapter. Later the dilator phase of vasomotion began to increase and the responsiveness of the metarterioles and precapillary sphincters to adrenaline diminished. Expressed in different terms the period of vasoconstriction following acute haemorrhage was superseded by a predominantly vasodilator phase with a concomitant loss of sensitivity of the blood vessels themselves to vasoactive stimuli.

They also described capillary stagnation due, not to mechanical obstruction such as met with in the acute phase, but to a generalized loss of tone in the microcirculation; it was a capillary rather than a venous stagnation though, venous stagnation inevitably added its effects as the state progressed. There was, in fact, a state of relaxation of arterioles, relaxation of capillaries and relaxation of venules, all filled with sequestered blood. On retransfusion some degree of tone returned transiently to the arterioles and precapillaries, but this was temporary and stagnation and backflow soon set in again, stasis of blood continuing until death.

Bellman, Lambert and Fine (1962), however, failed to observe any changes in the mesentery of rabbits during prolonged hypotension and oligaemic shock. The technique used was that of Chambers and Zweifach. They observed sludging in the mesentery under examination, but this was clearly artefactual because new exposed portions of the mesentery showed a normal circulation. When death occurred, blood flow stopped in a second or two without any preceding sign of disturbance in flow. They consider that the mesenteric circulation in the rabbit, at any rate, is well maintained in hypotension and shock.

Some of these discrepancies may well be explicable in terms of species difference. In the authors' own experience the rabbit is much more resistant to haemorrhagic shock than the dog; on the other hand, the dog presents anatomical peculiarities with respect to its hepatic veins not possessed by the rabbit. It is perhaps not surprising that the two species react differently. However this may be, the evidence concerning resistance changes in the gastrointestinal tract is far from consistent. Some authors report reduction in resistance, others no change. Most of the evidence would seem, however, to lead to the conclusion that little change occurs in intestinal or mesenteric resistance during the shock state. That is perhaps a surprising conclusion and it is one which must be considered in relation to the wider question of "pooling".

"POOLING" AND HUMORAL FACTORS IN OLIGAEMIC SHOCK

The splanchnic circulation has been implicated in oligaemic shock in one or other of two ways. In the first place the splanchnic bed, in particular the mesenteric bed, has frequently been described as the site of "pooling" of blood (i.e. of retention of sequestered blood) after long exposure to sustained low blood pressure. This retention of substantial volumes of blood in an already hypotensive animal may be regarded as perpetuating a vicious circle, the end result of which can only be death through a volume of circulating blood which is inadequate relative to the capacity of the peripheral circulation. The second implication of the splanchnic area concerns the means whereby terminal circulatory collapse is produced and depends upon the elaboration by an anoxic liver of substances inhibitory to vascular reactivity.

Pooling in oligaemic shock

The concept of pooling is used in one or two ways. In the first place there is extravascular pooling, namely the retention of blood in compartments (usually in the mesenteric vasculature) which, for the time being at least, are not in contact with the general circulation. The second, looser, use of the word simply means venous engorgement due to increased resistance to flow, with or without loss of vascular tone.

The observations of Wiggers *et al.* (1946) and Selkurt *et al.* (1947) clearly support the concept of pooling in the dog. In the rat, Kelan and Zweifach (1954) noted mucosal hyperaemia frequently in shock and found that removal of the gastro-intestinal tract and liver minimized the compensatory uptake of blood in prolonged hypotension. The implication of the venous bed as a site of pooling is made clear by the work of Alexander (1955). In spite of this evidence and the attractiveness of the concept, attempts to obtain quantitative data about pooling have been disappointing. Johnson and Selkurt (1956) found that an increase in bowel weight during shock occurred in some of their experiments but that it was not a necessary accompaniment. The experiments of Reynell *et al.* (1955)

and Friedman (1961) are even more discouraging, for they found that splanchnic plasma volume was reduced in shock and took the view that the splanchnic area actually contributes to the systemic circulation. Splanchnic plasma volume in these experiments was measured by the use of I^{131}-labelled serum albumin, and is a measure of circulating plasma. If blood were to be sequestered in the mucosa of the bowel and a large part of the intestinal flow were to be carried by arterio-venous shunts as suggested by Gouriz and Nickerson (1960), it seems likely that this method would be unsuitable for its detection.

The method should, however, record a large plasma pool in the venous bed; the fact that it does not is further evidence supporting the conclusion that splanchnic pooling is not a fundamental mechanism in the production of shock.

Vasodilators in oligaemic shock

Shorr, Zweifach and Firchgott (1945) suggested that under conditions of oxygen deprivation vasotropic substances might be produced in kidney and liver. Vasoexcitor material (V.E.M.) produced in the anoxic kidney was thought to be an early result of severe hypotension. Its action was to increase the sensitivity of the met-arterioles and to produce the effects of a generalized vasoconstriction, thus helping to maintain blood pressure and, by reducing the capacity of the peripheral circulation, stave off total collapse. The liver was thought to be involved later in the process when a sufficient degree of anoxia favoured the production of a vasodepressor material (V.D.M.) which had the opposite effect on the circulation. V.D.M., later identified as ferritin, was produced not merely in the anoxic liver but also in other tissues. Liver, however, was the sole tissue involved in its detoxication. This function was lost when the degree of anoxia was sufficient. The action of V.D.M. coupled with a reduced entry of V.E.M. into the general circulation as renal blood flow declined, was thought to be one of the main factors in the circulatory failure which constitutes "shock".

Without elaborating in further detail the ramifications of the hypothesis, sufficient has been said to illustrate its appeal. Accumulation of V.D.M., by relaxing hepatic arterioles might well cause increased portal pressure in the manner already discussed; it could account for the relaxation of mesenteric arterioles and, indeed, arterioles throughout the body. It could also account for the irreversibility of shock, for the fact that in an animal in "shock"—although its blood pressure be restored temporarily by retransfusion—inevitably the blood pressure declines and death supervenes from peripheral circulatory failure. Support for this concept was given by Frank, Seligman and Fine (1946), who found that if portal perfusion were maintained at normal levels in shock, irreversibility could be prevented, and by Cohn and Parsons (1950), who maintained liver blood flow in shock by an aortic-portal vein anastomoses, and again found better survival of shocked dogs.

Frank, Jacob, Friedman, Rutenburg, Glotzer and Fine (1952), however, failed to observe any shock-producing effect on intravenous infusion of V.D.M. into dogs in which nephrectomy and hepatectomy had been performed.

Selkurt (1959) has investigated the matter further. He concluded that livers made anoxic in shock do not contribute to irreversibility and stated that they were more likely to have a protective role. He produced evidence suggesting that vasodepressor agents were released, not from the liver, but from the bowel, these vasodepressor substances being destroyed by the liver. Thus in shock he was able to isolate vasodilator substances from the portal vein but only vasoconstrictor substances in the arterial blood. Terminally, vasodilator substances were also found in the arterial blood.

Blattberg, Maldonado and Levy (1960) have given some rather unconvincing support to the concept that the intestine may elaborate vasodilator substances in shock. They found that if the intestinal circulation in the hypotensive dog was perfused with donor blood, 5 out of 14 animals survived. Autoperfusion of the intestinal circulation led to recovery of 2 out of 22 animals.

More recently, Selkurt and Rothe (1962) have shown that although the gut may elaborate vasodilators in shock, these substances are not the lethal agent. Alexander (1963) considers that "it would seem high time to call off the search for something which has never been shown to exist, and which has been proven not to be there".

We have reviewed a cross-section of a large volume of work on the role of the splanchnic circulation in hypotension and in shock. The simple view was that the splanchnic area is a major partner in what may be termed the labile peripheral resistance and that in this role it is a principal factor in the preservation of systemic blood pressure; secondly when the hypotensive stresses are too great, from being a protective element the splanchnic area provides the wherewithal for vascular pooling and by the elaboration of vasodilator materials leads to the irreversible stage of "shock".

Unfortunately it is now abundantly clear that such a simple view of the splanchnic circulation is no longer tenable. As a partner in the labile peripheral resistance its role is doubtful. That the gastro-intestinal tract does possess sympathetically mediated vascular tone is undoubted; that this tone can increase with lowering of blood pressure is also generally agreed, but its effect vis-à-vis the systemic circulation is less certain. The extent of the changes which occur in the gastro-intestinal tract in response to altered blood pressure are, themselves, less than might be expected from a tissue vitally concerned in blood pressure regulation (*vide* Chapter IV). Nevertheless they are considerably more definite than are the changes in overall splanchnic blood flow reported in the present chapter. This alone, suggests some mechanism in the splanchnic circulation which offsets the effect of changes in gastro-intestinal vascular tone. One possible mechanism might be autoregulation, not perhaps a highly developed characteristic in the bowel vessels, but possibly more so in the liver. Then there is what now appears to be a well-authenticated reciprocity between hepatic arterial and portal venous flow whereby diminutions in portal venous flow are accompanied by increments in hepatic arterial flow—and vice versa. Even if hepatic and gastro-intestinal autoregulation are incomplete, such reciprocity can only mean that a change in vascular resistance in the gastro-intestinal tract brought on by changing blood pressure must be partially offset by the opposite effect in the hepatic vascular bed. Regarding the splanchnic circulation as a whole as a system of parallel resistances (Fig. 2.1) this can only serve to diminish the effectiveness of the gastro-intestinal tract as a useful factor in the labile peripheral resistance.

Although some of the above detailed considerations may be regarded as in part speculative, in the matter of total splanchnic flow the weight of the evidence must lead to the reluctant conclusion that the splanchnic area plays a far smaller role in the maintenance of peripheral resistance than has been generally assumed.

In the case of prolonged haemorrhage the degree of implication of the splanchnic area is even more doubtful. There is a strong probability that species differences account for some of the discrepancies found in the literature but, with the possible exception of the dog, the tempting hypothesis that "pooling" is essential to the genesis of shock must be discarded. Moreover the concept of the splanchnic area as the site of production during haemorrhage of lethal substances can no longer be supported.

X

THE SPLEEN

Blood supply, innervation and microstructure of the spleen

The spleen is an organ which varies considerably in gross anatomy according to the species. The macroscopic variations mainly concern such matters as relative size, presence or absence of a capsule, details of innervation and the precise relations of its afferent or efferent blood supply.

In man it is a soft, friable structure of variable size lying between the fundus of the stomach and the diaphragm. It is almost entirely surrounded by peritoneum which adheres firmly to its capsule. Folds of peritoneum forming the lieno-renal ligament and the gastrosplenic ligament connect it to the posterior abdominal wall and the stomach respectively, the space between the two layers of the former forming the avenue of access for its vessels of supply. The human spleen is well encapsulated; it is the internal fibro-elastic coat (as distinct from the external, serous coat) which forms the capsule proper. This consists of collagenous white fibrous tissue and yellow elastic fibres with many smooth muscle fibres in between. From the capsule many trabeculae pass deep and form the framework of the spleen. They, too, consist of fibrous, elastic and muscle fibres and together with the capsule constitute the contractile elements of the spleen, proper. Again, the relative proportions of elastic tissue to muscular tissue are species variable. In species where muscle tissue is predominant, active contraction of the spleen is a possibility, i.e. in such species the state of tone of the splenic musculature may itself determine the size of the spleen and, hence, the volume of blood it contains. In other species with relatively scant muscular elements dilatation or contraction of the spleen will be passive, and determined by the elastic tissue it contains, the pressure of the blood and the tone of the splenic vasculature.

It should be noted that in man there are few muscle fibres in the capsule or trabeculae.

The blood supply derives from the splenic artery, itself a branch of the coeliac artery with anastomotic connections to the left gastric and left gastro-epiploic arteries. Within the lieno-renal ligament the splenic artery breaks up into five or more branches, which vary from species to species, and ramify in the substance of the spleen. The nerve supply has been described in Chapter I. There is a sympathetic innervation but no evidence of a vagal supply.

The splenic arteries and veins are enclosed in a thick fibrous sheath derived from the capsule. After a short course, the artery becomes separated from the accompanying vein, but retains its sheath and becomes the trabecular artery, which divides repeatedly within the trabeculae. When the artery has reached a diameter of about 0·2 mm, it leaves the trabeculae, loses its fibrous sheath and becomes surrounded by a sheath of lymphoid tissue (Malphigian corpuscle) which collectively considered, constitutes the white pulp. An extensive capillary network supplies the pulp and the vessels are said to contain pores which allow the free entrance of lymphocytes into the blood (Moore, Mumaw and Schoenberg, 1964). The terminal branches of the follicular artery lose their lymphoid envelopes and enter the red pulp as a brush of precapillary arterioles, or penicilli. When these vessels reach a diameter of 5μ, they lose their muscular coat, and become surrounded with an ellipsoid sheath (Schweigger-Seidel, 1863). The fate of the terminal capillaries after leaving the sheath is uncertain. They may end freely in the meshes of the reticulum of the red pulp (as advocated by the proponents of the "open circulation") or communicate directly with venous sinuses (closed circulation). The arteries of the spleen are end arteries, there being no anastomoses with each other except at the hilus periphery, where inside the spleen there is a zone of communication (Volkman, 1923).

The veins of the spleen begin as networks of venous sinuses which penetrate the red pulp. They have a wide diameter ($12–40 \mu$). The walls of the sinuses are said to contain slit-like pores (McKenzie, Whipple and Wintersteiner, 1941) and are supported by a circular system of reticular fibres which are continuous with those of the pulp. The venous sinuses empty into the veins of the pulp, which coalesce to form the veins of the trabeculae and which unite to form the splenic veins.

The intermediary splenic circulation

The nature of the splenic circulation between the arteries and venous sinuses has been a subject of controversy for over 100 years.

There are three main theories as to how the blood reaches the sinus.

(*a*) That the arterial capillaries connect directly with the venous sinuses—the closed circulation (Billroth, 1862).

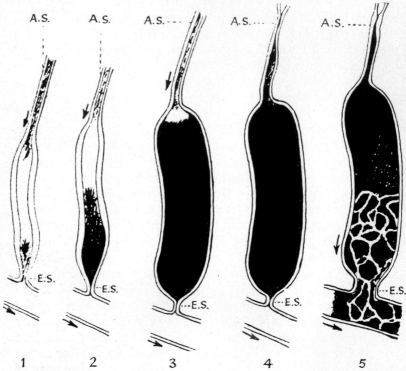

FIG. 10.1. Diagram to illustrate Knisely's concept of closed splenic circulation. Changes in blood sinuses during filling, storage and emptying phases—constructed from observations on transilluminated, exteriorized spleen. A.S.—afferent sphincter on afferent arteriole; E.S.—efferent sphincter at junction of capillary sinus and venule. 1. Free flow from afferent arteriole through sinus to venule (conduction phase). 2. Efferent sphincter beginning to close and sinus filling. 3 and 4. Efferent sphincter shut and sinus filled. Plasma escapes and red corpuscles are retained. 4. Represents the established storage phase. 5. Emptying phase—efferent sphincter relaxed and thick, paste-like contents of venous sinus discharged into the venule.

(Knisely, 1936.)

(*b*) That the arterial capillaries open directly into the pulp space, blood is thus postulated as having direct access to extravascular spaces from which it is filtered into the venous sinuses—open circulation (Robinson, 1926).

(c) That the circulation is closed in a contracted spleen but may become open when the spleen is distended (Klemperer, 1938).

Transillumination studies of the spleen by Knisely (1936) and McKenzie *et al.* (1941) have added to the controversy. Knisely described the splenic sinus in mice, rats and cats as an expanded segment of the endothelial tube connecting an arterial capillary with a venule. By the valve-like action of "physiological" sphincters situated at the afferent and efferent ends of every sinus, it passed through cycles of activity (see Fig. 10.1). Constriction of the sphincter at the efferent end of a sinus caused blood cells to accumulate within it and become packed into a relatively solid mass, the blood plasma passing rapidly through the walls of the sinus. Just before the sinus was quite filled, the sphincter located at its afferent end constricted to relieve it of the arterial pressure while it was packed with blood cells.

This storage phase is followed by sudden opening of the sphincter at the efferent end of the sinus and the discharge of masses of thick, pasty blood into the efferent venule. The afferent venule opens soon after and allows whole blood to enter and wash out the sinus. During the conducting phase which follows, whole blood courses through the sinus as through an arterial capillary. These findings are agreed by some workers, notably Peck and Hoerr (1951) and by Nakata (1954). McKenzie *et al.* (1941), however, using a transillumination apparatus similar to that of Knisely, with mice, rats, guinea pigs and cats, were unable to see either the intact sinus walls or the sphincters described by Knisely. According to their account, the only pathway between arterial capillary and a venous sinus is the "Zwischenstuck" or canal through the reticular cells (Fig. 10.2). Nowhere in the pulp did they observe an intact endothelial tube connecting the arterial and venous system. They did not find evidence for the cyclic activity described by Knisely. Their concept of blood flow through the spleen was similar to that proposed by Robinson (1926) in that they considered it to be primarily controlled by the musculature of the capsule and trabeculae and secondarily by arteriolar constriction. MacNeal (1929) and Riedel (1932) assumed that the ellipsoids of Schweiger-Seidel acted as valves which prevented the reflux of blood into the arterioles during splenic contraction. Wiedenreich (1901) considered that the ellipsoids acted by preventing too rapid an inflow of blood into the pulp. McKenzie *et al.* found that the peri-arterial sheaths in mice, rats, rabbits and guinea pigs were not concerned with the circulation. In the cat, however, structurally distinct ellipsoids were seen

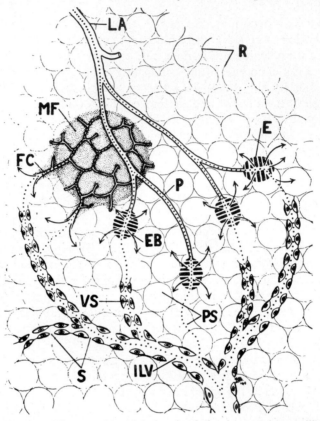

FIG. 10.2. Diagram of intralobular circulation in cat spleen to illustrate concept of "open" circulation. Arrows radiating from ellipsoids and follicle capillaries suggest a few of the pathways by which blood may traverse the pulp interstices in relaxed or distended spleen. Dotted lines indicate short-cuts taken by most of blood when spleen is contracted and the circulation is functionally closed.

LA—lobular artery; MF—Malpighian follicle; P—penicillus; FC—follicle capillary; E—ellipsoid; EB—lateral channel in wall of ellipsoid; R—red pulp reticulum; PS—pulp spaces; VS—venous sinus; ILV—intralobular vein; S—stomata in walls of venus sinus and intralobular vein.

(MacKenzie *et al.*, 1941.)

which were said to filter and distribute much of the blood entering the pulp. The activities of the ellipsoids were synchronized with splenic contraction and penicillar constriction.

An attempt to resolve these differences has been made by Snook

(1950), who studied the vascular arrangements of spleens from a large number of different species, by means of a special reticular staining technique. He considered that there were two types of spleen which he called sinusoidal and non-sinusoidal. In the sinusoidal spleen, which corresponded to the closed circulation pattern and which he found in the rat, guinea pig, rabbit, dog and man, the red pulp was an elaborate anastomosing plexus of true sinuses. In

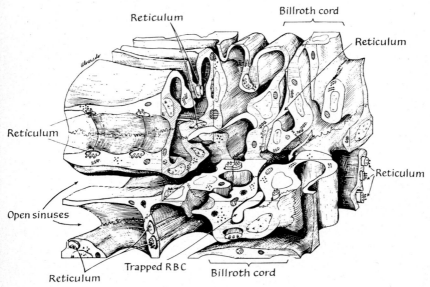

FIG. 10.3. Structure of the spleen as derived from electron microscopic studies. Open sinuses formed by littoral cells (macrophages and reticulum cells) intimately associated with reticulum. Sinus cavities communicate freely. Communications are present between tissues outside the sinus (Billroth cords) and the sinuses (white arrow). Reticulum forms a supporting framework for the sinus walls.

(Galindo and Freeman, 1963.)

the non-sinusoidal spleen corresponding to the open circulation pattern and found in mice, moles, cats, horse and cow, a few branched veins lead from the pulp meshes into the collecting veins.

One of the difficulties in accepting a closed circulation in the spleen is that there are large numbers of red cells in the pulp, which are not formed by erythropoeisis, and substances injected in the splenic veins enter the pulp and not the arteries. Electron microscopy studies by Weiss (1963) and by Galindo and Freeman (1963) have shown an essentially closed system with a number of openings in the sinus wall in the spleen of rabbits. Furthermore they considered that the tissues outside the sinus, Billroth Cords, are composed of vascular spaces formed by the same cellular and extracellular elements as sinuses. These spaces forming a sort of "outer tube" surround and communicate with the sinuses (Fig. 10.3). They receive some arterial blood. Weiss (1963) prefers to consider them as part of a vascular pattern and not as extravascular tissue.

If this view be confirmed it might provide a compromise answer to the old controversy between "open" and "closed" circulation patterns. In a sense both views would be correct. On the one hand there would be a direct vascular channel through which blood could pass from the penicilli to the venous sinuses. On the other there would be direct access to closed vascular spaces situated outside the main channel of through flow. The relative balance between these vascular provisions is probably species variable and, moreover, which is the more evident on microscopic examination of the spleen, must also be a function of its state of contraction.

METHODS USED IN THE STUDY OF THE SPLENIC CIRCULATION

Volume change

The first observations on the spleen were made by Wagner (1849) and by Henle (1852), who noted that the spleen could change size. Roy (1881) introduced the first quantitative measurements by means of an "onchometer" which was a visceral plethysmograph. He made measurements of splenic volume in cats and dogs. The method has the disadvantage of requiring manipulation of the organ after operation, and there is the danger of kinking the splenic vessels. Barcroft, Harris, Orahovarts and Weiss (1925) outlined the spleen with metal clips in the dog and used radiography to demonstrate change in spleen size in the conscious animal. Barcroft and Stephens (1927) also exteriorized the spleen and made direct observations of spleen size in the conscious dog. Bacq and Fredericq (1935) used a myograph to record splenic contraction in the dog and cat. Kramer and Luft (1951) recorded splenic weight continuously in the dog as an index of spleen blood content. Celander (1954) estimated changes in spleen size in the cat by laying the spleen of the anaesthetized animal upon a photographic plate.

Spleen volume measurements were used by Barcroft *et al.* (1925) as an indication of reservoir capacity. They cannot be used as an index of blood flow. They are a composite of many factors. In the words of Grindlay, Herrick and Mann (1939) "... when contraction of the spleen has occurred the commonly held opinion is that the blood flow is depressed. This is true after contraction produced by haemorrhage or certain drugs. It is not true for the splenic contractions produced by exercise, cold, ether, anaesthesia, noise and occasionally epinephrine ... it is clear that the behaviour of blood flow cannot be interpolated from plethysmographic data in the case of the spleen. ...."

Measurement of blood flow in splenic artery and vein

Burton-Opitz (1908*b*) used the mechanical stromuhr for the recording of blood flow from the splenic vein. The thermostromuhr was used by Mertens (1935) but the most comprehensive application of this method was by Grindlay, Herrick and Mann (1939). They used thermostromuhr units to measure blood flow in the splenic artery or vein in conscious dogs. In other experiments they made simultaneous recordings from both artery and vein of the anaesthetized animal. The information thus obtained enabled them to determine changes in both flow and in blood storage.

Ottis, Davis and Green (1957) have measured simultaneous splenic artery and vein flow in the dog by means of electromagnetic flowmeters and Green *et al.* (1960) have made similar measurements with the addition of continuous recording of splenic weight. Daly and Scott (1961) have described a preparation in which arterial inflow and spleen volume were recorded simultaneously. The spleen of a dog, enclosed in a plethysmograph, was perfused from the femoral artery of the same dog and splenic venous blood returned to the femoral vein. Arterial inflow was recorded with a rotameter.

In these measurements of arterial or venous flows the spleen was always separated from its vascular connections with the stomach and all tributaries of the splenic vein ligated.

Observations on the microcirculation

Knisely (1936*b*) used the quartz rod technique to illuminate the spleen and to visualize directly the blood flow of the intrasplenic vessels. Observations can only be made at the extreme edge of the spleen, and in animals which have thin spleens (mice, rats, guinea pigs and cats). The difficulties of the technique have been emphasized by McKenzie *et al.* (1941). Great care must be taken with temperature control and handling of the spleen.

A number of methods of less positive value have been used. The clearance of radioactive substances has been used by Sapirstein *et al.* (1960) to determine spleen blood flow in the rat, and heat exchange methods have been used by Grayson and Mendel (1957*a*). Radio-angiography has proved of clinical rather than of physiological importance in the study of the splenic circulation.

FUNCTIONS OF THE SPLEEN

The spleen is an organ of many functions, many of them beyond the scope of the present work. Its reticulo-endothelial functions— haemopoeisis at certain stages of life, erythrocyte destruction and phagocytosis at others—are of first importance; its relation to the immune reactions of the body is likewise important.

Our present concern, however, must be mainly with its relations to the circulation and the portal circulation in particular. In this context it has two principal functions. The first is as a store of blood, available to the general circulation. The second is as a communication linking aorta and portal vein. It has also been suggested that the spleen itself might elaborate vasoactive substances.

The spleen as a store of blood

That the spleen might serve as a store of blood was suggested as long ago as 1723 by Stukeley. The same suggestion is to be found in the work of Dobson (1830), of Gray (1854) and of Crisp (1855). These views were largely based on observations of splenic contraction following haemorrhage. Such observations did not, however, really prove the spleen to be a blood store in the sense which that phrase was later to acquire.

It was really the work of Barcroft and his co-workers which first provided evidence of actual storage of blood in the spleen, that is of sequestration of blood in storage spaces away from the mainstream of blood flow.

Thus Barcroft and Barcroft (1923) used carbon monoxide administration to show that a long period of time was required before carboxy-haemoglobin appeared in the splenic pulp. They stated, ". . . It would appear, then, that much of the spleen pulp is a sort of 'backwater' in which large quantities of corpuscles can be held. In this respect it differs from the liver in which if the corpuscles stagnate to any extent they do so in such close contact with the general circulation that the time taken for the carbon monoxide to diffuse into them is inappreciable by the methods used in the above research."

Barcroft and Barcroft showed, moreover, that carbon monoxide kills a splenectomized animal more quickly than one intact. Barcroft and Florey (1928) showed further that not merely does the spleen store blood but it also produces haemoconcentration in the stored blood through a draining off of plasma.

Further evidence of sequestration of blood in the spleen came from the work of Hanak and Harkavy (1924), who showed an increase in the amount of sequestered blood in the spleen during sleep. The observations of Knisely (1936), who observed microscopically the reaction of sinusoids and capillaries, added further weight to these concepts of blood storage. Amongst other observations he described the storage of blood cells in the spleen sinusoids during resting conditions.

The extent of storage

Barcroft (1926) reported that in dogs splenic contraction could increase total blood volume by 6–15 per cent. Izquierdo and Cannon (1928) found that in cats, excitement produced an increase of over 25 per cent in the red cell count which they ascribed to discharge of blood from the splenic reservoir. Kramer and Luft (1951), using the weight of the dog spleen as an index of its contained blood, showed that as a result of anoxia, the spleen could liberate a volume of blood equivalent to 16–20 per cent of the normal blood volume. The haemoglobin in the circulation increased by 10·5 per cent, indicating a store of about 40 g of haemoglobin in the spleen.

In recent years, however, doubt has been expressed concerning the role of the spleen as an emergency store of red corpuscles in man. Thus Parson, Mayerson, Lyons, Porter and Trautman (1948) say ". . . there is now considerable evidence that in man there are no reserves of blood or blood cells which are subject to emergency mobilization. In spite of these observations there has been considerable reluctance to abandon the earlier concept of splenic reserve of red blood cells as set forth by Barcroft in his original work on animals."

The evidence on which this view is based is largely derived from observation following the systemic administration of adrenaline. If the spleen of man functioned as an effective blood store it might be expected that an injection of adrenaline would lead to a detectable alteration in the blood picture. There should be some change at least in the relation between the plasma and its cellular content. A number of workers (Kaltreider, Meneely and Allen, 1942; Ebert and Stead, 1941) have performed this type of investigation and failed to find any convincing alterations which would support the hypothesis of red corpuscle mobilization. Similar observations were repeated by Parson *et al.*, who conclude, "If sympathetic stimulation or adrenaline influence these functions (i.e. red corpuscular mobilization), the effect must be very slight and of no real significance as an emergency response."

These findings emphasize the need for caution in extrapolating from one species to another. Dog spleen, on which most of the work leading to the concept of blood storage was performed, differs from human spleen in the amount of muscle it contains. There may well be other differences. Meanwhile, although further work is probably needed before the concept of blood storage in man is discarded altogether, such concepts must be viewed with caution.

Magnitude of spleen blood flow

Values for spleen blood flow obtained by different methods for the dog and rat are shown in Table 10.1. Total values found by Burton-Opitz using the mechanical stromuhr are similar to those found by Ottis *et al.* (1957) with the electromagnetic flowmeter. The average spleen weight given by Burton-Opitz was 58 g, compared with 345–394 g reported by Ottis *et al.* (for slightly larger dogs). It is not clear why the average spleen weights should be so different. One result is that the values for flow/100 g spleen weight given by Burton-Opitz are higher. The values obtained by Grindlay *et al.* (1939) with the thermostromuhr are unusually high compared with other methods. The absolute value for spleen blood flow in the rat found by Sapirstein *et al.* (1960) is small but in terms of tissue weight appears to be substantially higher than in the dog.

EFFECT OF VASOACTIVE SUBSTANCES ON SPLEEN VOLUME AND BLOOD FLOW

Adrenaline and noradrenaline

There is little doubt that adrenaline and noradrenaline reduce splenic volume, but the detailed effects upon the artery and vein are controversial. Oliver and Schafer (1895) first observed that extract of the suprarenal gland reduced the volume of the spleen of the dog. This was confirmed by Schafer and Moore (1896) for the dog and cat. Hunt (1918) found that in the perfused spleen of the cat and dog, adrenaline reduced the outflow. Mertens (1935), using

TABLE 10.1

Values for spleen blood flow

Author	Species	Flow, ml./100 g/ spleen/min	Total flow, ml./min	Method
Burton-Opitz (1908b)	Dog	58	31	Stromuhr
Grindlay et al. (1939)	Dog	—	97	Thermostromuhr
Ottis et al. (1957)	Dog	10	34-39	Electromagnetic flowmeter
Sapirstein et al. (1960)	Rat	—	0.5	Isotope fractionation

the thermostromuhr in the dog, claimed that adrenaline increased venous outflow more than arterial inflow, but that the increase in outflow was a consequence of splenic contraction. Following the initial increase in flow there was a drop in flow in both artery and vein which gradually returned to normal. Similarly Grindlay *et al.* (1939), using the thermostromuhr, found that 5 μg adrenaline/kg/ body weight, increased spleen artery flow by 20 per cent and splenic vein flow by 217 per cent in the conscious dog. Holtz and Schumann (1949) measured spleen volume in dogs and cats and found that intravenous adrenaline(0.5–1 μg) increased blood pressure and decreased spleen volume. Similar responses were obtained with noradrenaline. Holtz, Bachmann, Engelhardt and Greiff (1952) proposed that adrenaline acted upon the capsule and trabeculae of the spleen and that noradrenaline acted upon the vessels. They suggested that a "Milzsperrre" mechanism was operative for the spleen in cats and dogs. Their argument was based on the observations that adrenaline produced marked contractions of isolated splenic strips, whereas noradrenaline in the same concentration caused only a small contraction; moreover small doses of noradrenaline (1 μg) actually increased spleen volume whereas adrenaline (1 μg) always caused a reduction in spleen volume in the cat and dog. It was not clear how much of the increase in splenic volume with noradrenaline was due to the change in blood pressure, or whether it was in part due to a reduction of splenic outflow. Saad (1935) had previously shown that adrenaline caused contraction of strips of spleen of humans, dogs, rabbits, cats and guinea pigs. Celander (1954) measured spleen volume of cats by photography of the exposed spleen and found that both adrenaline and noradrenaline caused contraction of the spleen, but that adrenaline was twice as effective as noradrenaline. The minimum effective dose of adrenaline was 0·2 μg/kg and maximal effects were obtained with 2 μg/kg.

It appeared then that adrenaline was a powerful constrictor of the spleen and noradrenaline less so. Any deductions about flow were difficult to interpret because of the changes in blood pressure which occurred. Ottis *et al.* (1957) have overcome some of these difficulties by injecting adrenaline and noradrenaline into the

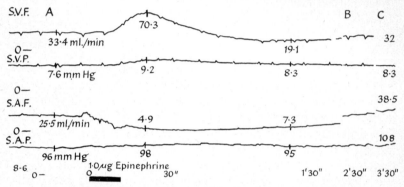

Fig. 10.4. The effect of intra-arterial epinephrine on splenic inflow and outflow in the dog. S.V.F.—splenic vein flow; S.V.P.—splenic vein pressure; S.A.F.—splenic artery flow; S.A.P.—splenic artery pressure. Flow figures are in ml./min and pressure figures are in mm Hg.

(Ottis, Davies & Green, 1957.)

splenic artery. They also measured splenic artery and vein pressures in addition to flow in the dog. The response to 1·0 μg of adrenaline injected into the splenic artery was to decrease splenic artery flow and to increase splenic vein flow (Fig. 10.4). This response was confirmed by Green *et al.* (1960). Noradrenaline acted similarly but was less effective. After blockade with phenoxybenzamine, adrenaline injected into the splenic artery now resulted in a small increase in splenic artery flow. This increase in flow could not be abolished by atropine. Comparison of arterial inflow and venous outflow before and after adrenergic blockade, with splenic nerve stimulation, adrenaline and noradrenaline, suggested that noradrenaline was concerned in the control of arterial inflow and adrenaline with venous outflow. The mechanism of the increased venous outflow was not clear, but they suggested it could result from venular dilatation and the elastic recoil of the wall of the sinusoids with the possible active contraction of smooth muscle in the substance of the spleen.

It appears then that the reduction in splenic volume with adrenaline is due to a reduction of arterial flow, combined with splenic contraction which empties blood from the spleen through a dilated venous bed.

One consequence of the increased venous outflow from the spleen with adrenaline is to lessen the magnitude of the fall in portal flow that also occurs. Grindlay, Herrick and Mann (1939) found that when the spleen was intact, portal flow fell by 37 per cent 30 seconds after 5 μg/kg adrenaline; the same dose of adrenaline produced an 87 per cent drop in flow after splenectomy.

Effect of acetylcholine

There is agreement that acetylcholine is constrictor to the smooth muscle of the capsule and trabeculae of the spleen, but here again, because of the difficulties in interpreting splenic volume, the effect on the vasculature is less certain. Fredericq (1929) showed that acetylcholine constricted isolated strips of canine spleen, a finding confirmed by Vairel (1933) for rabbits and guinea pigs and by Holtz *et al.* (1952) for dogs and cats. Saad (1935) found that acetylcholine sometimes contracted splenic strips of the human, dog, cat, rabbit and guinea pig, but if the tone was increased by adrenaline, acetylcholine then produced relaxation. He found that the effect of acetylcholine was abolished by atropine. Changes in volume of the spleen in the intact animal are difficult to interpret because of associated changes in blood pressure. Hunt (1918) measured splenic volume in the cat and found that 0·5 μg of acetylcholine intravenously caused a reduction of splenic volume followed by expansion, such that the final volume was greater than the initial volume. With the perfused spleen, acetylcholine gave a prolonged increase in outflow. He considered acetylcholine to be vasodilator and the initial fall in volume to be a result of the fall in blood pressure. Bacq and Fredericq (1935) found that with the denervated spleen of the dog and cat deprived of adrenal glands, acetylcholine produced only a slight increase in volume. Gotsev (1936) injected acetylcholine (3 mg) into the jugular vein of dogs and found a contraction of the spleen and a fall in blood pressure. After atropine, the blood pressure was unchanged but there was still splenic contraction, so that he considered the reduction in volume to be independent of blood pressure. Similar results were obtained in the cat.

Ferguson, Ivy and Greengard (1936) found that 1 mg acetylcholine in the dog caused contraction of the spleen, the contraction being unrelated to the fall in blood pressure. They considered the effects to be purely constrictor.

In order to avoid the difficulties created by the effects of acetylcholine on blood pressure, Faber (1936) injected acetylcholine (5 μg–1·0 mg) into the splenic artery of the dog. The spleen constricted and in two experiments he noted an after-dilatation similar to that observed by Hunt. He further showed that part of the effect of acetylcholine was mediated nervously. In a preparation in which the spleen of one animal was perfused by carotid–jugular anastomoses with a second dog, he cut the spinal cord of the dog in which spleen volume was measured and injected acetylcholine intravenously into this dog. The spleen contracted, and since acetylcholine was unable to reach the spleen directly, he suggested that acetylcholine stimulated a centre in the spinal cord to cause splenic contraction.

Observations on the blood flow to the spleen have shown that the local action of acetylcholine is vasodilator. Grindlay *et al.* (1939), using the thermostromuhr in conscious dogs, found that intravenous acetylcholine (1·0 mg) caused an increase in splenic artery and vein flow. The difficulties of changes in blood pressure, portal pressure, nervous stimulation and adrenal stimulation have been overcome by the use of the isolated spleen perfused from the donor animal, acetylcholine being given into the splenic artery. Green, Ottis and Kitchen (1960) measured splenic artery and vein flow and splenic artery and vein pressures, in a similar preparation using dogs. Acetylcholine (1–3 μg) injected into the splenic artery resulted in an increase in both inflow and outflow. The changes in inflow were greater than the changes in outflow so that the volume of the spleen increased. Atropine reduced the response but did not abolish it.

Daly and Scott (1961) perfused the dog spleen, which was contained in a plethysmograph, with blood from the femoral artery and returned the splenic venous blood to the femoral vein. Arterial inflow was measured by means of a rotameter, and splenic artery and vein pressures were also recorded. Small doses of acetylcholine (0·01–5 μg) injected into the splenic artery caused a decrease in vascular resistance and a small increase in splenic volume of about 5 ml. The effects were abolished by atropine. The changes in spleen volume were considered to be a passive effect of the dilatation of

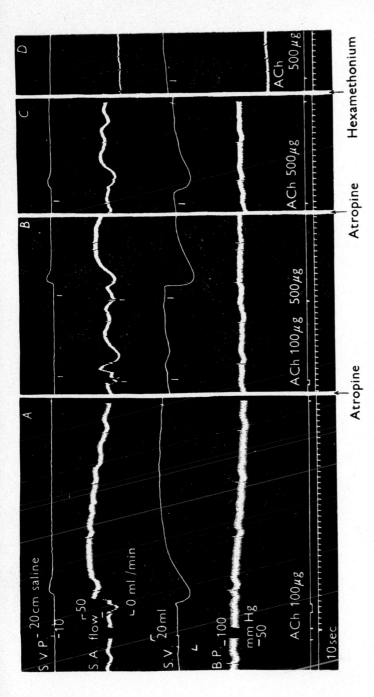

Fig. 10.5. Perfusion isolated spleen—dog. Effects of close arterial infusions of acetylcholine. Between A and B atropine, 2 mg injected i.v. Between B and C atropine repeated, 2 mg. Between C and D hexamethonium—10 mg/kg—i.v. S.V.P.—splenic vein pressure. S.A.—splenic artery flow. S.V.—spleen volume. B.P.—arterial blood pressure.

(Daly and Scott, 1961.)

the splenic vessels. This result is in substantial agreement with Green *et al.* (1960). Larger doses of acetylcholine (5–100 µg) were of interest. There was a reduction of splenic volume (of the order of 20–30 ml.), but this was not abolished by atropine, and was attributed to the nicotine-like action of acetylcholine (Fig. 10.5). If the nicotine effect was abolished by hexamethonium, acetylcholine still caused contraction which was abolished by atropine, suggesting a muscularine-like action directly on the splenic capsule. The nicotine-like action of acetylcholine was abolished by symptholytic drugs and by degeneration of the nerves to the spleen. It seemed likely that the nicotine-like effect of acetylcholine was due to release of adrenaline and noradrenaline from stores surrounding the sympathetic nerve endings. Large doses of acetylcholine always lowered vascular resistance. It seems clear then that acetylcholine in small doses is vasodilator to the spleen and a passive increase in volume may be expected to occur. Larger doses of acetylcholine caused splenic contraction by a direct effect upon the capsule and possibly by the release of adrenaline and noradrenaline from the spleen. Since the amounts of acetylcholine used in earlier experiments were very variable, the contradictory results obtained, and the conflicting reports in relation to atropine are explained by the work of Daly and Scott.

Histamine

The effect of histamine on spleen volume was first investigated by Dale and Laidlaw (1910) in the cat. Histamine caused a fall in blood pressure and a reduction in splenic volume, but splenic volume recovered before the blood pressure. Ferguson *et al.* (1936) found that with a dose of histamine sufficient to cause a fall in blood pressure, there was a reduction in splenic volume. Smaller doses which did not affect blood pressure did not affect spleen volume. They considered the effect on spleen volume to be secondary to the fall in blood pressure. Grindlay, Herrick and Mann (1939) gave 1·0 mg histamine intravenously to the dog and found a marked reduction in splenic arterial flow and a fall in splenic venous flow which was preceded by a brief increase. Blood pressure was not recorded. According to Krafka, McCrea and Vogt (1929) the spleen does not contract during anaphylactic shock.

It would seem that histamine has little effect on the spleen or splenic vasculature, most of the effects described can be ascribed to changes in systemic blood pressure.

Pituitrin

Magnus and Schafer (1901*b*), Dale (1910), Hargis and Mann (1925) and Barcroft (1926) showed that extracts of the posterior lobe of the pituitary caused a reduction in splenic volume. Boer and Carrol (1924*b*) considered the reduction of splenic volume to be due to vascular constriction rather than a contraction of the smooth muscle of the capsule. They perfused the spleen of the cat by means of a constant output pump and found that pituitrin decreased the venous outflow without a decrease in splenic volume. Grindlay *et al.* (1939) found that 0·05 mg pitressin given intravenously to the dog caused a sudden reduction in arterial inflow and a more gradual reduction in venous outflow. It seems likely from these results that pituitrin is constrictor to both the smooth muscle of the capsule and to the splenic vasculature.

NERVOUS CONTROL OF SPLENIC VOLUME AND FLOW

Sympathetic stimulation

One of the earliest observations of the effect of nervous stimulation on splenic volume was that of Wagner (1849), who noted that the spleen of the dog contracted on direct stimulation. Henle (1852) showed that the spleen could contract in man. Schiff (1867) obtained contraction of the spleen in rabbits and cats on stimulation of the splanchnic nerves. Tarchanoff (1874) noted that stimulation of the medulla oblongata or either splanchnic nerve caused contraction of the spleen in dogs. Roy (1881) similarly found contraction of the spleen in dogs and cats and noted further that when the vasomotor centre was stimulated there was a rise in blood pressure and reduction of splenic volume. Section of the splanchnic nerves did not affect spleen volume. Schafer and Moore (1896) confirmed that contraction of the spleen occurred when the splanchnic nerves were stimulated and showed that the 5th–9th thoracic roots were particularly involved in the sympathetic innervation of the spleen. Celander (1954) has emphasized the low frequency of sympathetic stimulation required to produce splenic contraction. In the cat, he found that stimulation with one impulse every 2 seconds caused a 15 per cent reduction in splenic volume, and 2 impulses/sec a 45 per cent reduction. Nerve stimulation was more effective in reducing splenic volume than the systemic administration of adrenaline or noradrenaline, which, in the case of noradrenaline, he suggested

was due to the fact that its access to the spleen was prevented by
the contraction of the spleen.

In connection with blood flow, Burton-Opitz (1908*b*) found that
splanchnic nerve stimulation caused a drop in splenic vein flow in

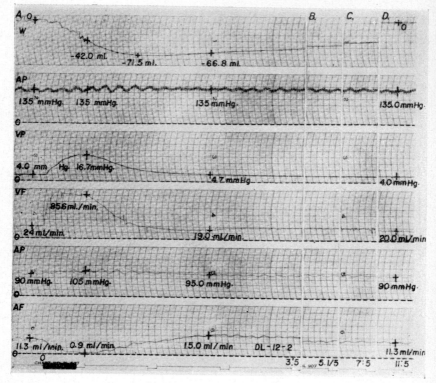

FIG. 10.6. The effect of splenic nerve stimulation on spleen weight,
splenic arterial inflow and splenic venous outflow in the dog. W—
splenic weight; upper AP—systemic arterial pressure; VP—splenic
vein pressure; VF—splenic vein outflow; lower AP—splenic arterial
pressure; AF—splenic arterial inflow. Signal at bottom—stimulation
of splenic nerve. Time in min.

(Green, Ottis and Kitchen, 1960.)

the dog. Green, Ottis and Kitchen (1960) recorded splenic artery
and vein flow with electromagnetic flowmeters and also recorded
splenic weight continuously. Splenic nerve stimulation with a frequency of 20 per sec resulted in a drop of arterial inflow from 11·3
to 0·9 ml./min and a rise in outflow from 24 to 85·6 ml./min. There
was a loss of weight equivalent to 42 ml. of blood (Fig. 10.6).
Blockade with phenoxybenzamine did not alter blood flow, but

reversed the arterial constriction with splenic nerve stimulation so that dilatation of the artery occurred. The dose of blocking agent required to reverse the response to nerve stimulation was similar to that required to reverse the response with noradrenaline. The increased venous outflow with splenic nerve stimulation or adrenaline was not abolished with large doses of blocking agent. Green *et al.* (1960) suggest that the arteries are supplied with α and β receptors and the transmitter is likely to be noradrenaline, and that the vein has β receptors and the transmitter is likely to be adrenaline.

Effect of the vagus

Apart from the observations of Roy (1881) it is generally agreed that the vagus does not affect the spleen. It will be remembered that there is no anatomical evidence for a vagal innervation. Bulgak (1877) made direct observations of the spleen in dogs and noted that stimulation of the cut thoracic vagus did not affect spleen volume, but that stimulation of the central end produced a strong contraction. He also noted that stimulation of the central end of the superior laryngeal nerve resulted in splenic contraction and considered the effect was due to a change in respiration. Roy (1881) noted that vagal stimulation caused contraction of the spleen, which was not related to the fall in blood pressure. Roy was under the impression that acute changes in blood pressure, in any case, did not affect spleen volume, because he found that occlusion of the aorta below the diaphragm did not affect spleen volume. He was unable to detect pulse waves on his plethysmograph tracings and considered that there was a high resistance to flow. Schafer and Moore (1896) found, however, that splenic volume was acutely affected if the aorta was constricted and thus pulse waves could be clearly seen. They could find no effect of vagal stimulation on spleen volume. Magnus and Schafer (1901a) found that vagal stimulation had no effect on the spleen in the dog, cat, rabbit or monkey. They suggested that the contraction reported by Roy was due to the spread of the stimulus. Matsuda (1927) found that in the cat, stimulation of the vagus caused a fall in blood pressure and splenic contraction. Stimulation of the sectioned vagus below the cardiac branches did not affect spleen volume. Stimulation of the central end of the cut vagus caused a fall in blood pressure and splenic contraction. Bacq and Fredericq (1935) also consider that the sympathetic is the only nerve supply to the spleen. They recorded spleen contraction in the dog and cat with a myograph and found that splenic nerve stimulation was not affected by eserine or atropine.

It is interesting to note that Dale and Dudley (1929) were unable to detect acetylcholine in the spleens of the dog, cat, monkey or rabbit, although they found evidence of ample acetylcholine in the spleen of the ox and horse. Chang and Gaddum (1933) confirmed these observations and estimated the acetylcholine in horse and ox spleen as from 4 to 30 μg/g of tissue.

Reflex control of spleen volume

There is general agreement that alterations in splenic volume may be brought about by baroreceptor reflexes. Thus, Gollwitzer-Meier and Schulte (1931) found in the dog that clipping the carotid artery, which raised the systemic blood pressure, caused a reduction in spleen volume. When the pressure in the carotid sinus was raised, blood pressure fell and spleen volume increased.

The efferent pathway of these effects has, however, given rise to some controversy. There remains some doubt as to the relative importance of adrenaline or noradrenaline release and of the sympathetic nerve supply to the spleen.

Heymans (1929) on the basis of cross-perfusion experiments in the dog adduced evidence showing that reductions in the spleen volume could be brought about by adrenal activity alone. Thelen (1933), Brauch (1934), Euler and Liljestrand (1935) agreed that spleen contraction could be so mediated. Since they failed to find increased blood glucose during splenic contraction they doubted whether adrenaline was the mediator. Holtz and Schumann (1949) also confirmed that carotid occlusion could cause spleen contraction without raising blood sugar or inhibiting intestinal motility. Since doses of adrenaline large enough to contract the spleen also inhibited gut motility and raised the blood sugar—which, in doses effective in reducing spleen volume, noradrenaline did not—they concluded that noradrenaline was probably the responsible agent.

Driver and Vogt (1950), however, did not agree on the importance of the adrenal gland. They found that changes in splenic volume following carotid occlusion were abolished by section of the nerves to the spleen but not by adrenalectomy. With the exception of one dog, they were unable to find an increased output of adrenaline in the adrenal vein after carotid occlusion. They concluded that the nerve supply to the spleen constitutes the main efferent pathway for the mediation of baroreceptor effects.

In general, then, it would seem established that in the dog, at least, spleen contraction occurs with baroreceptor reflexes. There is evidence for a nervous mediation, there is also evidence suggesting that liberation of noradrenaline by the adrenal gland may be a factor.

RHYTHMICITY OF THE SPLEEN

It was noted by Roy (1881) during studies of volume changes in the spleen of cats, dogs and rabbits, that there were rhythmical changes in spleen volume. The rhythm of the changes was variable, the fastest waves being at 44-sec intervals and the slowest at 2–3-min intervals. Volume changes of the order of 5 ml. were found, which Roy calculated to be about 18 per cent of the spleen volume, although occasionally decreases of 36 per cent were seen. These waves coincided with blood pressure changes, a decrease in volume being associated with a rise in blood pressure and a relaxation with a fall in blood pressure, which made it unlikely that the spleen changes were secondary to the blood pressure change. The splenic rhythm persisted after splenic nerve section. Schafer and Moore (1896) confirmed the presence of rhythmic variations in volume and that the waves persisted after splanchnic nerve section. In fact after nerve section they were more pronounced. They considered that the waves were due to inherent rhythmic contractility of the spleen. Barcroft and Nisimaru (1932) showed that if the splenic artery was clamped, both the splenic rhythm and undulations in the blood pressure were prevented. They considered that the rhythmic variations in splenic volume were responsible for the blood pressure changes.

More recent evidence does not uphold this view. The rhythmic changes in splenic volume do not appear to be due to the capsule but to vascular events in the spleen. Loewe and Faure (1925) found that isolated strips of splenic capsule did not exhibit rhythmicity. Mertens (1935) and Grindlay, Herrick and Baldes (1939) showed by means of thermostromuhrs on the splenic artery and vein, that rhythmical changes in blood flow in the artery and vein were responsible for the changes in volume. Although the magnitude of the variations in artery and vein flow were identical, there was a lag of 5 sec in the venous fluctuation which was enough to explain the changes in splenic volume.

THE SPLEEN IN HAEMORRHAGE

The spleen has been frequently evoked as a major organ in the body's defences against haemorrhage. Much has already been said in this chapter on the question of spleen contractility. Nevertheless there is perhaps need to review further the possible role of the spleen in haemorrhage.

There are three considerations. In the first place there is the question of the spleen as a store of blood, a question related to the whole matter of contractility and the control of contractility. There is the question of blood flow responses in the spleen apart entirely from the matter of contractility and liberation of stored blood. Then there is the final question of the spleen as an organ which may or may not elaborate vasoactive substances.

The contraction of the spleen in haemorrhage was reported by Dobson (1831), Gray (1854) and Crisp (1855). Barcroft, Harris, Orahovarts and Weiss (1925) showed that the major diminution in spleen volume in the cat occurred at the beginning of haemorrhage. In the dog the liberation of blood was more gradual. From what has already been said it is clear that baroreceptor mechanisms and adrenaline or noradrenaline secretion may all be involved, resulting in the discharge of stored blood into the general circulation. Grindlay, Herrick and Mann (1939) found that a haemorrhage of 10·6 per cent of the total blood volume in the dog in $2\frac{1}{2}$ min led to a fall in spleen arterial flow from 59 to 27 ml./min. A bleed of 30 per cent of the total blood volume in 3 min reduced venous outflow to near zero levels.

Grayson and Mendel (1957a) recorded liver blood flow by internal calorimetry in the rat and determined the effect of occluding the splenic pedicle at different blood pressure levels (Fig. 8.3). With mean systemic blood pressure levels of 140 mm Hg, splenic vein occlusion had little effect on liver blood flow. When the mean systemic blood pressure had been lowered by haemorrhage to 80 mm Hg, occluding the splenic vein now produced a 20 per cent reduction in liver blood flow. At lower pressures the splenic contribution to liver blood flow again became negligible. Sapirstein et al. (1960) studied spleen blood flow in the rat by means of clearance of radioactive rubidium. From their data it has been estimated that the contribution of splenic blood to total splanchnic blood flow was 4·3 per cent when the systemic blood pressure was 120 mm Hg, 4·8 per cent when the blood pressure was 90 mm Hg and negligible when the blood pressure was 28 mm Hg. The reasons for these discrepancies are not apparent but it is at least clear that both at normal and at low blood pressure levels the contribution of the splenic vein to total splanchnic flow in the rat is small.

Graanat (1953) has questioned the concept that the volume of blood released by the spleen during haemorrhage is responsible for the maintenance of blood pressure, and suggested that a pressor substance is released by the spleen. He injected 10–80 ml. of blood into the portal vein of dogs and found that there was no change in blood pressure. Adrenaline and noradrenaline injected into the splenic artery of dogs had a much greater pressor effect than similar injection into the splenic vein, and the effect was more prolonged than that obtained by injecting adrenaline or noradrenaline into a femoral vein. When splenic extracts were injected into the splenic artery, portal or femoral vein a response was obtained which resembled the effect of noradrenaline but was more prolonged. He considered that the effect of splenic contraction was to release noradrenaline into the blood but considered an additional vasoactive substance was present to explain the prolonged response. Lofving and Mellander (1955) measured the response of the nictitating membrane of the cat as an index of smooth muscle constricting substances in the circulation. They could not confirm the presence of such a substance in the blood stream on stimulating the splenic nerves.

The spleen in shock

Henderson (1910) and Erlanger and Gasser (1919) suggested that during haemorrhagic shock pooling of blood occurred in the spleen. Lewis, Werle and Wiggers (1943), however, have shown that in haemorrhagic shock in the dog, the spleen remains constricted and continues to be so on re-infusion. In so far as recent opinion is opposed to the general concept of pooling there would seem little cause to invoke the spleen in the "shock" syndrome.

THE EFFECT OF ANOXIA

Schafer and Moore (1896) found that during asphyxia in the dog, the spleen contracted and that the mechanism was reflex, for if the spleen was denervated, there was dilatation as a consequence of the rise in blood pressure. Boer and Carrol (1924a) investigated the mechanism of splenic contraction with carbon monoxide poisoning in the cat. They found that carbon monoxide poisoning caused splenic contraction independently of changes in blood pressure. The excised spleen dilated when perfused with blood containing carbon monoxide which they attributed to the effect of anoxia on the splenic capsule. They showed further that carbon monoxide was ineffective in causing contraction of the spleen if the nerve supply was destroyed. The adrenal gland and pituitary were not involved. In cats in which the spleen was perfused with Ringer's solution and the nerve supply left intact, carbon monoxide poisoning of the animal led to splenic contraction. It was evident that the mechanism was nervous and they suggested that anoxia acted on the spinal cord. Kramer and Luft (1954) found that in the dog there was a reduction in splenic weight when the oxygen saturation was reduced to 40 per cent.

THE EFFECT OF DIET

Prolonged changes in splenic volume are said to occur after feeding. Dobson (1830) found that the splenic volume of the dog increased in the 4th hour after feeding and the increase persisted for a further 8 hours. Hargis and Mann (1925) studied spleen volume, using a plethysmograph *in situ* in the conscious dog. Both carbohydrate and meat feeds increased the splenic volume but meat was particularly effective, a rapid increase in volume occurring which lasted for 7–8 hours. Grindlay, Herrick and Mann (1939) found that after feeding both arterial and venous flows increased by 26–100 per cent and the effect lasted for 3–5 hours. The mechanism responsible for the increase in flow is unknown.

THE EFFECT OF EXTERNAL STIMULI

Stimuli of many kinds have frequently been shown to affect the spleen. Thus, sudden noises, which frighten the animal, have been shown to be a potent stimulus to spleen contraction in the dog (Hargis and Mann, 1925). They termed this response the "splenic reflex". Conversely rest and sleep produce spleen dilatation and favour storage of blood in the spleen (Grindlay, Herrick and Mann, 1939). Barcroft and Elliot (1936) showed that fear produced splenic contraction in the dog even after denervation. They also showed that exposure to cold led to splenic contraction. Grindlay, Herrick and Mann (1939) found an increase in both arterial and venous flow with decrease in external temperature.

Exercise also brings about splenic contraction (Barcroft and Stevens, 1927; Barcroft and Elliot, 1936). Grindlay, Herrick and Mann (1939) found an increase in splenic artery and vein flow during exercise in the dog. Since it is known that adrenaline or nervous stimulation reduce arterial inflow, the rise found by them was presumably due to a rise in blood pressure.

The effect of anaesthesia has not been extensively investigated, but according to Hausner, Essex and Mann (1938) ether contracts the spleen while barbiturates dilate the spleen.

THE SPLENIC-LIVER FACTOR OF REIN

According to Rein, the spleen releases a substance during stimulation of the splenic nerves which on passage through the liver exerts a beneficial effect on the myocardium. Rein (1949) found that the changes in blood pressure and venous pressure produced by breathing 7 per cent oxygen in the dog, were affected by the presence of the spleen. Thus blood pressure during anoxia was better maintained, and the onset of cardiac failure, as indicated by the rise in venous pressure, was delayed in the presence of the spleen. Rein (1951) claimed that this splenic factor could affect the response of the myocardium after severe temporary coronary occlusion. In the dog, graded occlusion of the right coronary artery led to a fall in blood pressure and a rise in right ventricular end diastolic pressure, followed by various types of arrhythmia. Rein measured the time required for these events to occur and the time taken for the circulation to recover after removal of the coronary occlusion. Splenectomy accelerated the rate at which these changes occurred, and splenic nerve stimulation or the injection of splenic blood from a donor animal delayed the onset of these events. Rein considered that a factor was present in the plasma of splenic blood which was released during nerve stimulation. The effect could not be produced by equivalent volumes of arterial blood.

One of the difficulties in interpreting this type of experiment is that splenic extracts appear to delay the onset of cardiac failure for periods of up to one minute. Responses to successive periods of coronary occlusion may differ in each control period and it may be difficult to produce precisely the same degree of coronary occlusion. In some experiments in which the splenic nerves were stimulated during the period of coronary occlusion, the blood pressure increased, which may have been due to the release of noradrenaline

(Graanat, 1953). The existence of a splenic-liver factor appears to be uncertain.

The vascular functions of the spleen have undergone substantial revision. There can be little doubt that Barcroft's concepts of the spleen as a contractile organ capable of storing considerable volumes of blood are substantially correct in many species. There is doubt as to whether they can be upheld in man. Species variations, both anatomical and physiological, account for many of the contradictions in the literature and great care must be exercised in extrapolating from one species to another.

The relationships of the spleen to the rest of the splanchnic circulation remain undefined. Grayson and Mendel (1957a) have postulated a view of the spleen as an organ supplying increased quantities of blood to the portal vein under conditions of falling blood pressure when the gastro-intestinal contribution itself is depleted. Their views, however, are insufficiently substantiated at present. One observation they have recorded, however, which is of interest is that rats can survive indefinitely after ligation of the hepatic artery; they can also survive indefinitely after removal of the spleen.

Ligation of the hepatic artery together with splenectomy always led to death within 24 hours. They give no explanation of this phenomenon but it does suggest some further functional link between spleen and liver.

XI

THE CONTROL OF PORTAL PRESSURE

THE portal vein, although thin-walled as compared with arteries, is yet thick and muscular compared with most veins (Walker, 1959). In function it is both the venous drainage channel of a very large vascular territory and the principal afferent supply of a vital organ which itself subserves many complex functions. Portal pressure is the outward expression of these often contrasting functions. It is the resultant of portal inflow and resistance to portal outflow modified by the splenic contribution to portal flow and the portal–systemic connections.

MEASUREMENT OF PORTAL PRESSURE

Francois-Franck and Hallion (1896) recorded portal pressure from simple cannulae inserted either in a mesenteric vein or in the splenic vein, using a saline manometer for recording. Simple techniques of this nature have been used to the present day in animals. More elaborate methods of manometry have occasionally been employed, but for most purposes a saline manometer is adequate.

The first measurement of portal pressure in man was by Thompson, Caughey, Whipple and Roussel (1937). They recorded portal pressure at open operation from a mesenteric vein. Shaldon (1960) has described a technique in which a cannula is left in a vein of the omentum and remains in place for some days.

In order to overcome the necessity for open operation Myers and Taylor (1951) introduced the technique of wedged hepatic pressure to evaluate the portal pressure in animals and man. They passed a catheter into the inferior vena cava and along the hepatic vein in the cat until it occluded the vein. They compared the resultant pressure with the pressure directly measured in the portal vein. They found good correlation, the difference being only 0·6 mm Hg. They claimed that a catheter wedged into a hepatic vein dams up a static column of blood extending from the hepatic vein to the junction of the portal venous blood on the other side of the sinusoid.

Friedman and Weiner (1951) found that in the dog, hepatic vein pressure is about 1 mm Hg higher than portal venous pressure. Paton, Reynolds and Sherlock (1953) found good agreement between occluded hepatic vein pressure and portal venous pressure in man, but Balfour *et al.* (1954) found that the pressure in the occluded hepatic vein was 4–5 mm Hg less than that in the portal vein in human subjects with portal hypertension of intrahepatic origin.

In cirrhotic patients with portal hypertension, Davidson, Gibbons and Faloon (1950) measured pressure in the portal venous system from a collateral vein in the abdominal wall. Oesophageal varices have been similarly used (Allison, 1951).

TABLE 11.1

Portal pressure, occluded hepatic vein and free hepatic vein pressures in different species

Author	Species	Portal pressure, mm Hg	Occluded hepatic vein pressure, mm Hg	Free hepatic vein pressure, mm Hg
Thompson *et al.* (1937)	Man	7–10	—	—
Welch *et al.* (1954)	Man	—	12·4	8·6
Myers & Taylor (1951)	Man	—	4·8	3·3
Paton *et al.* (1953)	Man	—	6·8	4·9
Burton-Opitz (1908*a*)	Dog	10·8	—	—
Friedman & Weiner (1951)	Dog	10·0	10·6	0·3
Wakim (1954)	Dog	5·3	—	1·6
Deal & Green (1956)	Dog	13·9	—	—
Torrance (1961)	Dog	8·6	—	—
Schmid (1908)	Cat	8·6	—	—
McMichael (1932)	Cat	7·4	—	—
Myers & Taylor (1951)	Cat	8·0	8·6	—
Nakata *et al.* (1960)	Rat	9·4	—	1·7–1·0

Table 11.1 compares portal pressure, wedged hepatic vein pressure and free hepatic vein pressures. Values for portal flow are shown in Table 4.1.

Intrahepatic pressure relationships

The most comprehensive study of this subject is by Nakata, Leong and Brauer (1960). They inserted micropipettes in rat livers and determined the pressure required to allow dye to enter vessels punctured under transillumination. Pressure in the mesenteric vein which they regarded as equivalent to portal pressure was 12·7 cm saline; in a portal venule it was 6·3 cm saline; in an hepatic venule it was 2·3 to 1·4 cm saline.

There was a substantial pressure drop across the sinusoid.

A further observation of interest was that vena caval pressure at the level of the hepatic veins could be higher than that in the hepatic vein. They attributed this to cyclic changes associated with respiration whereby there was a cessation or even a reflux of blood flow from the hepatic veins in inspiration, forward flow taking place in expiration.

Origins of portal blood

The venous drainage of the bowel begins in the large venous plexus which is situated between the base of the glands and the muscularis mucosa. In the stomach, the organ in which these re-lationships have been established in the greatest detail, the veins of the stomach penetrate the muscularis mucosa and join the veins draining other parts of the stomach. From the venous arcades which are thus formed are derived the gastric and mesenteric veins which drain into the portal vein. A feature of this venous system is that the veins draining the stomach and colon are endowed with valves, whereas the veins draining the small intestine have no valves. The functional significance of this curious provision is not known.

A number of factors affect the flow of blood into these venous channels. One is the tone of the gastro-intestinal capillaries. Another is the action of the arterio-venous shunts described by Barclay and Bentley (1949). Rhythmic contractions of the villae are another factor propelling blood into the venous plexus. Finally, it has also been suggested that the muscularis mucosa can act as a sphincter and, by contracting or relaxing, exert some control on inflow into the veins (Walder, 1954).

The venous drainage of the bowel is, of course, not the only source of portal blood. The circulation to the mesentery itself with its profusion of central channels and arterio-venous anastomoses supplies an additional quantity of portal blood. Moreover the curi-ous anatomical configuration of the mesenteric circulation, already considered in detail elsewhere in this work, offers the possibility of blood storage.

The spleen is also a minor contributor of blood and when the systemic arterial pressure is normal probably has little effect on portal pressure. When the systemic pressure is lowered to levels of about 80 mm Hg, however, it has been suggested that the contribu-tion of the spleen to portal flow and to portal pressure may be greater. At these levels there is even the possibility of an increased blood flow through a contracted spleen.

The spleen, too, has a significant importance as a blood store in some species and the liberation of stored blood can have marked, though transient, effects on portal flow and pressure. Such effects are seen when sudden falls occur in systemic blood pressure.

Regulation of portal outflow

The outflow of blood from the portal system is largely presided over by the liver. We have already considered in some detail the regulation of liver blood flow. We shall not reiterate in any detail what has already been said, but certain aspects of this problem need restating from a different point of view.

The work of Nakata *et al.* (1963) makes it clear that the portal venules and the sinusoids constitute the major resistance to portal outflow. Post-sinusoidal resistance varies with species, and in the dog, for example, the existence of hepatic venous sphincters is clearly important. Sphincters do not exist as such in man.

Another factor for consideration is that portal pressure may be partially dependent on hepatic arterial pressure. This may come about in two ways. Firstly, since the hepatic arterial blood is under far higher pressure than the blood in the sinusoids, the extent of the hepatic arterial flow may be expected to affect directly the pressure in the sinusoids. Secondly, any patent hepatic arterial–portal venous communication may directly transmit pressure from the arterial system to the portal vein.

Finally, there is the question of portal–systemic communications such as occur in the oesophageal plexus and the haemorrhoidal plexus of veins. These communications have been of clinical rather than of physiological interest. The existence of an "overflow" system of this nature in the control of portal pressure cannot be ignored. Its function as an emergency route or "run-off" operating in the event of blockage of the portal vein is already clear from clinical observation. Probably of more direct physiological importance, however, are the retro-peritoneal veins (the veins of Rhetzius) which, according to Edwards (1951), are normally patent.

The delayed compliance of the mesenteric vein described by Alexander *et al.* (1951) is an additional factor which probably serves to prevent sudden rises in portal pressure.

GENERAL FACTORS AFFECTING PORTAL PRESSURE

Vasoactive substances

The effect of adrenaline on portal pressure is illustrated by the experiments of McMichael (1932) using cats. He found resting levels of portal pressure of about 7·0 mm Hg. He showed that adrenaline caused an initial rise in portal pressure due to constriction of the portal ramifications in the liver. This was followed by a secondary rise resulting from increased mesenteric and hepatic arterial inflow due to an increased blood pressure.

In man the responses are somewhat different (Shaldon, Peacock, Walker, Palmer and Badrick, 1961). Adrenaline, given by infusion into a jejunal vein, produced an initial fall in portal pressure due to mesenteric vasoconstriction. This was followed by a sustained rise (Fig. 11.1) which could have resulted from two effects. One

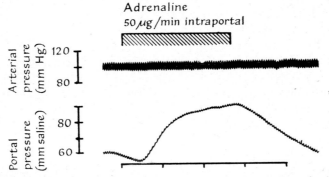

FIG. 11.1. The effect of an infusion of adrenaline into a jejunal vein in man.

(Shaldon, Peacock, Walker, Palmer and Badrick, 1961.)

was constriction of the portal radicles increasing hepatic resistance to portal outflow; the other was a raised systemic pressure sufficient to swamp the local vasconstrictor effect of adrenaline and produce an increased flow through the gastro-intestinal circulation into the portal vein. Of these two factors the former seemed to be the more important since infusion into the portal vein produced only a slight increase in systemic blood pressure (adrenaline is totally destroyed in the liver and such an infusion, at least in the doses used by Shaldon *et al.*, has no systemic effect).

McMichael (1933) reported that acetylcholine was without effect on the portal pressure. Katz and Rodbard (1939), however, showed

that large doses produced a fall in systemic blood pressure accompanied by a fall in portal pressure. This may well be due to the
relationship which has been shown to exist between mean systemic
arterial pressure and portal pressure (Grayson and Mendel, 1957a;
Torrance, 1961), a fall in the former leading directly to a fall in the
latter. A further factor may also be the vasodilator effect of acetylcholine on the liver reported by Ginsburg and Grayson (1954).

The effect of extracts of the posterior lobe of the pituitary gland
have received some attention. Oliver (1897) reported that they produced constriction of the mesenteric blood vessels. McMichael
(1932) showed that pituitary extracts caused a fall in portal pressure
which was due to a reduction in portal inflow. These findings have
been confirmed by Chakravati and Tripod (1940) and by Wiggers
et al. (1946) in the dog and in man by Walker (1961).

Histamine has also been investigated in relation to portal pressure. Mautner and Pick (1915) reported a swelling of the liver.
Bauer *et al.* (1932) confirmed the swelling of the liver and a rise in
portal pressure in the dog. This was thought to be due to constriction of the sphincters since in species devoid of sphincters neither
swelling of the liver nor rise in portal pressure occurred. Wiggers
et al. (1946) also confirmed a rise in portal pressure with histamine,
but although he accepted a rise in hepatic resistance, he felt the
main reason for the rise in portal pressure was dilatation of the
mesenteric vascular bed.

Systemic arterial pressure and portal pressure

In special circumstances, e.g. the action of adrenaline referred
to above, portal pressure and systemic arterial pressure may alter
in different directions. Nevertheless, apart from such specialized
situations there is a general relation between systemic arterial
pressure and portal pressure.

There are two major channels through which the systemic
arterial pressure could mechanically influence portal pressure. One
is through the mesenteric circulation, the other through intrahepatic communications between hepatic artery and portal vein
(i.e. either through the sinusoid or through hepatic arterial–portal
venous anastomoses).

Grayson and Mendel (1957a) measured portal pressure in rats
by means of a saline manometer and mean systemic arterial pressure with a mercury manometer. They reported a linear relationship between mean systemic arterial pressure and portal pressure

during alterations in systemic pressure produced by haemorrhage. Subsequent observations (Grayson and Mendel, unpublished) show in fact that the relation is not always linear. Fig. 11.2 gives the results of two experiments showing the limits found in the relationship. Similar results were found even after ligation of the hepatic artery (Grayson and Mendel, 1957*a*).

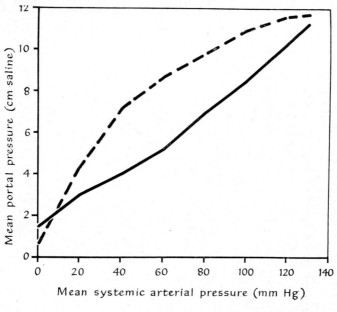

FIG. 11.2. The relationship of mean portal pressure and mean systemic arterial pressure in the rat.

(Grayson—unpublished observations.)

When the hepatic artery is intact it is possible that some of the relationship may be due to back transmission of pressure to the portal vein from the hepatic artery. In perfused liver, Andrews *et al.* (1955) demonstrated such a transmission. Similar findings were reported by Torrance (1961), who found a sigmoid relationship between hepatic arterial and portal venous pressures (Fig. 11.3) in the dog when hepatic arterial perfusion pressure was altered independently of systemic arterial pressure. Friedman and Weiner (1951) found that portal pressure in the dog—which was 10 mm Hg—fell by 0·7–2·0 mm Hg on clamping the hepatic artery. Grayson and Mendel (1957*b*) found similar falls in portal pressure on clamping the hepatic artery of rats. Walker (1961) showed similar falls in portal pressure on clamping the hepatic artery in man.

Direct transmission of pressure across the liver can thus account for about 25 per cent of the portal pressure in animals. There is some evidence, however, which suggests that the pressure transmission can be considerably higher than this. Thus Grayson, Ginsburg and Walker recorded portal pressure from the splenic vein of

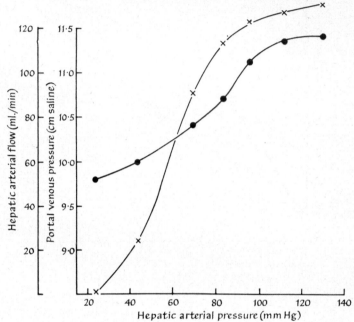

FIG. 11.3. Relationship between portal venous pressure and hepatic arterial pressure (closed circles) compared with the relation between hepatic arterial flow and hepatic arterial pressure (crosses). Dog. (Torrance, 1961.)

rats and observed the effect of clamping the superior mesenteric vein (quoted by Grayson, 1954). In about half of the experiments the result was merely a decline in recorded pressure but, in the remainder, portal pressure rose to levels as high as 14–22 mm Hg, values double or treble resting levels. It was thought that this was due to direct pressure transmission probably through opening up of arterio-venous anastomotic communications.

It would seem from the evidence that the contribution of hepatic artery to portal pressure is an important determinant and it is conceivable that in pathological states it might be even more important.

APPENDIX

HEAT EXCHANGE METHODS IN THE MEASUREMENT OF BLOOD FLOW

HEATED thermocouples were first introduced into the measurement of blood flow by Gibbs (1933). In the first instance the heated thermocouple was intended to be used in intact vessels in much the same way as the thermostromuhr. It consisted of a thermocouple mounted in a needle and heated by an attached filament of constantan wire through which a constant current was passed. In artificial systems it was shown that the faster the flow of fluid through a tube, the lower the recorded temperature; the slower the flow of fluid, the higher the recorded temperature. The instrument, being needle mounted, was designed to be inserted intravenously, so as to measure blood flow in veins. Unfortunately it proved to have all the disadvantages of the thermostromuhr without sufficient merit of its own to warrant its general application as a flowmeter.

Later it was applied to the qualitative determination of blood flow change in solid organs. Schmidt and Pierson (1934) applied this method to an investigation of blood flow in the central nervous system. The principle of use was the same. With a steady heating current, the greater the flow of blood past the instrument, the lower the recorded temperature; the slower the flow, the higher the recorded temperature. Used in this way the instrument could only give results capable of purely qualitative interpretation (Schmidt and Pierson, 1934).

More recent applications of the methods, however, although using instruments of very similar design, depend upon somewhat different treatment of the findings.

In 1952 Grayson showed that it was possible to use heated thermocouples for the determination of thermal conductivity of any tissue or material into which they could be inserted. He was able to demonstrate that Carslaw's (1921) relation for heat losses from a sphere in an infinite mass of material could be applied to observations from the heated thermocouple. Thus the relation

$I^2 = F.\theta.k$ (where $I =$ the heating current; θ is the temperature increment produced by the heating current; k is the thermal conductivity and F an instrumental constant) was valid provided sufficient tissue or material surrounded the probe. As a means of the physical measurement of thermal conductivity the usefulness of this technique has been abundantly demonstrated and has never seriously been questioned. The data published in this respect are remarkably consistent. Most tissues such as liver and muscle which are predominantly protein–water gels give thermal conductivities of $11\cdot7$–$12\cdot0 \times 10^{-4}$ c.g.s. units whatever method is used. In explanation of this consistency, it is possible that, "the relation between total protein and water content in an animal tissue is probably a major factor in determining its thermal conductivity" (Grayson, 1952).

Over a very much wider range of conductivity than occurs in animal tissues, Grayson has demonstrated linearity between the instrumental recording by the methods to be described and thermal conductivity as determined by other methods.

The difficulty comes in assessing the relationship between blood flow and the recorded findings.

From the point of view of blood flow determination, the method depends on the claim by Grayson that over any likely biological range of flow the relationship between recorded thermal conductivity (which contains two elements, one being the actual conductivity of the tissue, the other an artefact produced by circulating blood) and flow is linear. He used "conductivity increment", namely, the recorded conductivity less the conductivity of dead tissue, as a direct measure of local blood flow in the vicinity of the probe.

In an analysis of the heated thermocouple technique, Bill (1962) says, "It therefore seemed a great improvement when Grayson reported that with a modification of Gibbs' procedure, it was possible to determine the apparent increase in thermal conductivity δk which was caused by the blood flow, and that δk was proportional to the flow." Grayson's claims, however, have been by no means universally upheld.

Thus Linzell (1953) says, ". . . results do not confirm Grayson's finding that the cooling of the probe is proportional to the blood flow except under certain restricted conditions". Bill summarizes the contradictions in the literature: "Experiments verifying or contradicting Grayson's findings concerning the relation between blood flow and δk have been repeatedly reported in the literature."

Before proceeding to a detailed analysis of the various techniques used, it is therefore proposed to consider the validity of the use of such heat exchange methods in the determination of blood flow.

There is some evidence to suggest that the relationship between blood flow and temperature rise in a heated thermocouple may not be strictly linear. Thus, Grayson showed (1951*a*) that the temperature responses of a heated thermocouple in a stream of fluid, although apparently linear over a moderate range of flow, fit better a logarithmic relationship, but this does not exactly match the circumstances of a heated thermocouple lying in a mass of tissue. In tissue perfusion experiments using heated thermocouples, the published data of Linzell (1953), Graf, Golenhofen and Hensel (1957), Kiese and Lange (1957) justify a straight line relationship between δk and flow over varying ranges of flow, although in each case a logarithmic relationship might produce a better "fit".

In fact, most of the published data derived from heat exchange methods have assumed that over the physiological range of flow, the relation between flow and thermal conductivity is linear.

In kidney perfusions, Linzell (1953) (who has been one of the leading critics of the technique) has shown approximate linearity between apparent thermal conductivity and flow with flow rates of up to 50 ml./100 g of tissue/min. In view of the difficulty in the kidney of assessing the total amount of actual vascular tissue involved, this is probably an encouraging figure. Hensel and his coworkers (see Graf and Rosell for references, 1958) have shown linearity in skin and sheep spleen with flow rates up to 100 ml./100 g tissue/min. Similar findings are reported by Mowbray (1959) for thyroid gland and muscle. In dog liver, Graf, Golenhofen and Hensel (1957) reported linearity for a saline perfusion in all experiments up to flow rates of 50 ml./100 g/min and in most up to 100 ml./100 g/min. These figures accord well with Grayson's findings on rat and rabbit liver where the outflow from the liver was measured directly and correlated with thermal conductivity, the flow being varied by imposed alterations in mean systemic blood pressure (Fig. 12.1). Here, too, linearity was obtained up to flow levels of 80–100 ml./100 g tissue/min. In heart muscle, Kiese and Lange report, too, linearity between thermal conductivity increment and flow up to flow levels of 100 ml./100 g/min.

As a qualitative measure of blood flow, thermal conductivity measurements have proved themselves useful. From a quantitative aspect, it is clear that caution must still be exercised. It would seem that over a moderate range of blood flow, assumptions of linearity are probably justified, but in tissues as vascular as the liver, the limits of usefulness are being approached.

On the other hand, it has become clear that for many reasons, in tissues of low vascularity, the method may be misleading. One simple consideration makes this clear. The thermal conductivity

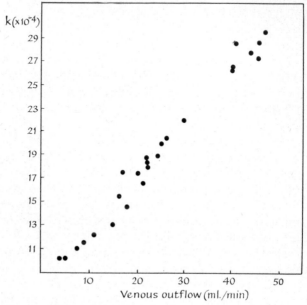

FIG. 12.1. The relations between liver outflow and thermal conductivity in the liver of the cat anaesthetized with nembutal.

increment in liver, where the flow may be as high as 100 ml./100 g/min, is rarely higher than 12×10^{-4} c.g.s. units. In tissues such as skeletal muscle where the flow is more of the order of 2 ml./100 g/min, the thermal conductivity increment might be expected to be of the order of 0.2×10^{-4} c.g.s. units. From the purely technical point of view, thermal conductivities of this order of magnitude are very difficult to record accurately. Also to be considered are the conclusions of Perl (1962) and of Bill (1962) which emphasize the importance of a rich capillary bed and the danger of misleading information when the main route of blood flow is through large vessels rather than capillaries. It seems then that subject to the loss of linearity at really high blood flow levels, heated thermocouple techniques are best applied to tissues of high vascularity.

The difficulties arising from the use of models for the evaluation of the relationship between flow and thermal conductivity have been emphasized by Perl, who points out that no one has yet produced anything approaching a working model of the microcirculation.

Nevertheless, the work of Bill, using complex models consisting of polythene tubes mounted in gelatine, shows that reliable results can only be expected from heated thermocouple techniques in tissues rich in capillaries where the chance influence of large vessels is minimized (such conditions as obtain, for example, in rat liver).

It also becomes clear from these model experiments that no consistent relationship between local thermal conductivity increment and overall tissue blood flow can be obtained on theoretical grounds. No model can reproduce the complexity of the microcirculation in the liver—or for that matter of any other tissue.

Given adequate caution in the interpretation of results, there are a number of unique advantages in the use of heated thermocouples. The probes are small, flexible and easily implanted in internal organs. They evoke little local tissue reaction (Johnson, 1953) and may be left *in situ* for weeks and even months, allowing continuing observation over very long periods. Experiments can be conducted on conscious animals; where the proposed experiment calls for an anaesthetic it may be carried out on an animal implanted days previously and in correspondingly better condition than would be the case if flow recorders had to be inserted at the same time.

THE TECHNIQUE OF INTERNAL CALORIMETRY

Heated thermocouple techniques seem to have a real place in blood flow investigations in tissues such as the liver. Accordingly a brief description of one of these methods—designated "internal calorimetry" by its author (Grayson, 1952)—will be given.

The semi-quantitative recording of blood flow using heated thermocouples depends on the determination of apparent thermal conductivity according to the relation

$$I^2 = F.\theta.k$$

In his original method, Grayson determined the I^2 value required to raise the tissue temperature by $1\,°C$ and maintain it at a steady state. He has since discarded this approach in favour of a method which determines the temperature elevation produced by a predetermined heating current (I^2 = constant).

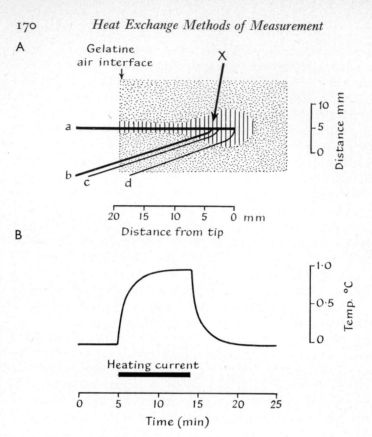

FIG. 12.2. To illustrate the principles of "internal calorimetry".
A. Diagram of probe in tissue (constructed from data in Grayson, 1952). Shaded rectangle—block of gel (10 per cent gelatine in water); a—constantan lead; b—copper lead from thermocouple; X—thermocouple; c and d—leads to heating circuit. Inner zone (vertical hatching) represents limits of detectable elevation of temperature in gelatine produced by passage of a constant heating current such as to raise the temperature of X by 1 °C above its initial temperature.
For the sake of clarity the various leads are shown separate. The temperature zones depicted in fact apply to a probe with all the leads in close alignment.
B. Temperature changes from point X produced by the switching on of a constant heating current. Temperature elevation = 1 °C. Time to equilibrium = 7 min. Time to return to base-line temperature = 7 min.
These times are similar in dead liver. With blood flowing the time to equilibrium is shortened. It is still too long for use in living tissues.

The practical difficulty of the technique is to find some method of compensating for possible changes in tissue temperature occurring during the period of equilibrium. In his approach, Hensel uses probes in which the reference junction is also mounted far enough from the heater for no interaction to occur. He claims, probably correctly, that when inserted into a tissue such as liver, temperature changes due to other than circulatory causes affect both heated and cold junction alike and that a continuous recording from the heated thermojunction will therefore give a continuous recording of thermal conductivity.

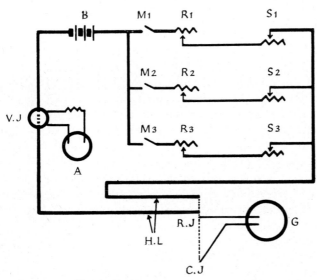

FIG. 12.3. Circuit diagram.
B—6 V, 100 amp hr accumulator. M_1, M_2, M_3—microswitches operated by cam from constant speed motor adjusted to produce the timing referred to in Fig. 12.4. R_1, R_2, R_3—decade resistances used to give approximately the currents required in each of the circuits. S_1, S_2, S_3—0 to 1Ω slide wire resistances for accurate adjustments of output currents. V.J.—vacuojunction to enable output currents to be read directly in A^2 on the ammeter, A. H.L.—heater leads. R.J.—recording thermojunction. C.J.—cold junction (usually inserted in blood supply to organ). G—galvanometer unit (Cambridge D'arsonval movements incorporated in multi-channel photographic recorder—Cambridge Instrument Co. Ltd.)

Grayson's method differs in that the "cold junction", the temperature reference point, is outside the tissue (where possibly it is situated in the blood supply to the organ). Changes in the temperature base are determined by applying a cyclic current to the heaters producing a record similar to that shown in Fig. 12.4 From one point, therefore, a record is obtained of the temperature of the tissue, (*a*) heated by a fixed current of 0·315 A^2; (*b*) heated by a current of 0·20 A^2. The difference between these two equilibria levels gives the temperature increment, produced by a current of 0·115 A². This achieves compensation for changes in tissue temperature without the necessity for incorporating the "cold junction" in the tissue. It has a further advantage in that the lower equilibrium temperature can be used for the determination of changes in tissue temperature due to non-circulatory factors, a value which, under controlled conditions, can be used as an index of metabolic heat production.

Fig. 12.2 illustrates the principles of the method.

Fig. 12.3 shows the electric circuits used.

For use in liver blood flow determination, the probe (which, in effect, is a flexible leash of copper and constantan wires) is implanted in the liver of the experimental animal at open operation. The leads are brought out through an incision in the back of the animal, as far as possible out of range of its teeth. The abdominal incision is then closed.

In most cases the presence of the probe caused little or no tissue reaction and healing was uneventful. Measurements could be made on the intact, conscious animal—or if further operation was indicated this could be carried out without the additional trauma of placing blood flow probes.

A typical record from a rat is shown in Fig. 12.4, together with the calculation of thermal conductivity. In his earlier work Grayson calibrated each probe in 10 per cent gelatine in water gels where the thermal conductivity was known. It has been abundantly shown, however, that the thermal conductivity of dead animal tissues varies very little from animal to animal—or even in different species. The thermal conductivity of rat, rabbit, monkey or human liver is about $11·8 \times 10^{-4}$. It is regarded as sufficient for most purposes, therefore, to use the reading from the dead liver as a calibration as indicated in the legend.

The method has also been applied to estimations of liver blood flow in man. Graf was probably the first to describe its use in this context using the Hensel modification which mounts the cold junction in the same probe as the recorder. Grayson and Kinnear (1962) extended this work. Probes were inserted into the livers of human volunteers using a subcostal approach under local anaesthetic. A biopsy needle was inserted into the substance of the liver, the probe (mounted in polyethylene tubing) was threaded through the needle, and the biopsy needle was withdrawn leaving the probe *in situ*. Its position was checked by X-ray. Being flexible the probe could be left in place for long periods of time during which continuous records of temperature or blood flow could be taken. In these experiments the "cold junction" was placed in the rectum. Each

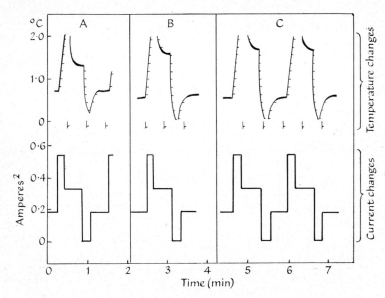

Fig. 12.4. To illustrate the automatic method of recording thermal conductivity in rat liver. Current supplied to the heater through an automatic contact maker (see Fig. 12.3) as follows: 0·20 A² for 24 sec; 0·60 A² for 17 sec; 0·315 A² for 24 sec, zero current for 17 sec, 0·6 A² and zero current provide periods of overheating and overcooling necessary to produce equilibrium levels of temperature corresponding to currents of 0·200 A² and 0·315 A². Temperature difference between upper and lower equilibrium levels gives temperature increment produced by current of 0·115 A². Formula $k = F.I^2/\theta$ can be applied.

A—animal anaesthetized with ether (B.P. = 130 mm Hg).
B—asphyxia (B.P. = 40 mm Hg).
C—death.

Assuming thermal conductivity of dead liver = 11·8 × 10⁻⁴ c.g.s. units, knowing $I^2 = 0·115$, measuring θ from the record, thermal conductivity may be calculated:

A—(anaesthetic); $k = 21·9$; whence δk (live reading less dead reading) = 10·1 × 10⁻⁴.
B—(asphyxia); $k = 13·1$; whence $\delta k \parallel 1·3 × 10⁻⁴$.

probe was standardized separately in 10 per cent gelatine in water gels and a mean value for dead liver thermal conductivity assumed in order to estimate k.

TISSUE HEAT PRODUCTION

A further extension of the Grayson method which, although not of direct concern to this work, materially extends the usefulness of the technique, is of interest.

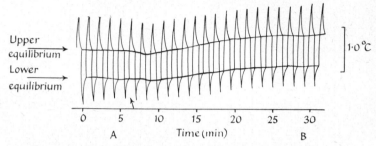

FIG. 12.5. Treatment of a record to obtain corrected temperature (i.e., temperature change brought about by non-circulatory factors). The continuous lines joining the various upper equilibrium levels and the lower equilibrium levels are construction lines added to the photographic record for ease of measurement. The vertical distance between these construction lines $= \theta$. (θ is the temperature rise produced by a heating current increment of $0.115 A^2$. It is a reciprocal function of the thermal conductivity.) At point A (before insulin), $\theta = 0.64°C$. Insulin administered at the arrow. At point B, $\theta = 0.69°C$. Between these two points, therefore, there was a fall in blood flow. There was also a rise in the lower equilibrium temperature. Since this is the temperature of a heated thermocouple, this rise in lower equilibrium temperature could, at least in part, have been due to the drop in blood flow. In order to estimate the rise in temperature produced by this change in blood flow, and consequently, in apparent thermal conductivity, the following calculation may be applied: at point A, $\theta = 0.64°C$. Under these conditions of apparent thermal conductivity, this is the temperature rise produced by a current of $0.115 A^2$. But lower equilibrium is produced by a current of $0.200 A^2$.

∴ at point A, tissue temperature was raised

$$0.200/0.115 \times 0.64°C \text{ by the heating current.}$$

At point B, if no change in heat production were to have taken place, nor any change in heat losses, then the lower equilibrium level should be

$$0.200/0.115 \times 0.69°C.$$

That is to say, circulatory change should have produced a temperature change between A and B of

$$0.200/0.115 \times (0.69 - 0.64)$$
$$= 0.09°C.$$

But in fact the temperature change which did occur, measured from the record, was $0.3°C$. The temperature change from non-circulatory causes was therefore $0.21°C$.

The cold junction was situated in the blood supplying the liver; the experiment was carried out under conditions of constant temperature; since no change in respiration was recorded, it is regarded as most likely that this temperature represents a change brought about by increased heat production.

In most of the recent animal work conducted by Grayson and his colleagues the temperature of the heated thermocouple was recorded with the cold junction in the blood vessels of supply to the liver. The lower equilibrium temperature is the temperature of the liver modified by the presence of a heating current, the effect of which in turn is modified by the circulation.

Between any two points on any record it is easy to measure the change in temperature which has occurred in the lower equilibrium. Such a change could be brought about by blood flow change, by alterations in heat loss, or by alterations in heat production. (Changes in blood temperature were compensated by the position of the cold junction—*vide supra*). A simple calculation, shown in Fig. 12.5, makes it possible to eliminate the blood flow factor. This is a calculation which depends only on thermal conductivity measurements. The relation between thermal conductivity and blood flow is not involved, nor is the thermal conductivity of dead tissue. The corrected temperature remaining is thus dependent on local heat production and heat losses from the liver only.

Under controlled experimental conditions it is possible to eliminate changes in heat loss. One is therefore left with calculated temperatures directly related to tissue heat production. As a qualitative index of heat production this approach has produced promising results. A further attempt made to express the results quantitatively (Dosekun, Grayson and Mendel, 1960) cannot, however, be regarded as having general applicability at present.

REFERENCES

ADAMS-RAY, J. and NORDENSTAM, H. (1958). Chromaffin cells in liver biopsy. In *Liver Function*. Ed. Brauer, R. W. Amer. Inst. Biol. Sci. Monograph No. 4, 274–277.

AHLQUIST, R. P. (1948). A study of adrenotropic receptors. *Amer. J. Physiol.* **153**, 586–600.

ALEXANDER, R. S. (1954*a*). The influence of constrictor drugs on the distensibility of the splanchnic venous system analyzed on the basis of an aortic model. *Circulation Res.* **2**, 140–147.

— (1954*b*). The participation of the venomotor system in pressor reflexes. *Circulation Res.* **2**, 405–409.

— (1955). Venomotor tone in haemorrhagic shock. *Circulation Res.* **3**, 181–190.

— (1956). Reflex alterations in venomotor tone produced by venous congestion. *Circulation Res.* **4**, 49–53.

— (1963). The Systemic Circulation, in *Annu. Rev. Physiol.* **25**, 213–230. Annu. Rev. Inc. California.

ALEXANDER, R. S., EDWARDS, W. and ANKENEY, J. L. (1953). The distensibility characteristics of the portal vascular bed. *Circulation Res.* **1**, 271–277.

ALLISON, P. (1951). The measurement of blood pressure in oesophageal varices. *Thorax*. **6**, 325–327.

ALMY, T. P. and TULIN, M. (1947). Alterations in colonic function in man under stress. Experimental production of changes simulating the irritable colon. *Gastroenterology*. **8**, 616–626.

ANDREWS, W. H. H. (1951). Pathological processes in malaria. Progress Report III. The hepatic lesion. *Trans. R. soc. trop. Med. Hyg.* **45**, 27–32.

— (1953). A technique for the perfusion of the canine liver. *Ann. trop. Med. Parasit.* **47**, 146–155.

— (1958). Functional differences between hepatic artery and portal venous regions. In *Liver Function*. Ed. Brauer, R. W. Amer. Inst. Biol. Sci. Monograph No. 4, 241–245.

ANDREWS, W. H. H., HECKER, R. and MAEGRAITH, B. G. (1956). The action of adrenaline, noradrenaline, acetylcholine and histamine on the perfused liver of monkey, cat and rabbit. *J. Physiol.* **132**, 509–521.

ANDREWS, W. H. H., HECKER, R., MAEGRAITH, B. G. and RITCHIE, H. D. (1955). The action of adrenaline, l-noradrenaline, acetylcholine and other substances on the blood vessels of the perfused canine liver. *J. Physiol.* **128**, 413–434.

ANDREWS, W. H. H., MAEGRAITH, B. G. and RICHARDS, T. G. (1956). The effect upon bromsulphalein extraction of the rate and distribution of blood flow in the perfused canine liver. *J. Physiol.* **131**, 669–677.

ANDREWS, W. H. H., MAEGRAITH, B. G. and WENYON, C. E. M. (1949). Studies on liver circulation: microanatomy of hepatic circulation. *Ann. trop. Med. Parasit.* **43**, 229–237.

ANREP, G., CERQUE, S. and SAMAAN, A. (1934). The effect of muscular contraction upon blood flow in skeletal muscle, the diaphragm and small intestine. *Proc. Roy. Soc. B*, **114**, 245–247.

AREY, L. B. (1932). On the presence of the so-called portal lobules in the seal's liver. *Anat. Rec.* **51**, 315–322.
— (1941). Throttling veins in livers of certain mammals. *Anat. Rec.* **81**, 21–33.
AUNAP, E. (1931). Ueb er den Verlauf der Arteria hepatica in der Leber. *Z. mikr.-anat. Forsch.* **25**, 238–251.
BACQ, Z. M. and FREDERICQ, H. (1935). Sur la nature de l'innervation de la rate. Action de divers agents pharmacodynamiques. *Arch. int. Physiol.* **41**, 322–333.
BAER, R. and RÖSSLER, R. (1926). Beiträge zur Pharmakologie der Leber-gefässe. *Arch. exp. Path. Pharmak.* **119**, 204–221.
BAINBRIDGE, F. A. and DALE, H. H. (1905). The contractile mechanism of the gall bladder and its extrinsic nervous control. *J. Physiol.* **33**, 138–155.
BAINBRIDGE, F. A. and TREVAN, J. W. (1917). Some actions of adrenaline upon the liver. *J. Physiol.* **51**, 460–468.
BALFOUR, D. C., REYNOLDS, T. B., LEVINSON, D. C., MIKKELSEN, W. P. and PATTISON, A. C. (1954). Hepatic vein pressure studies for evaluation of intrahepatic portal hypertension. *A.M.A. Arch. Surg.* **68**, 442–445.
BARCLAY, A. E. and BENTLEY, F. H. (1949). The vascularization of the human stomach. *Brit. J. Radiol.* **22**, 62–67.
BARCROFT, H. and LOUGHRIDGE, W. M. (1938). On the accuracy of the thermo-stromuhr method for measuring blood flow. *J. Physiol.* **93**, 382–400.
BARCROFT, J. (1926). Die Stellung der Milz im Kreislaufsystem. *Ergebn. Physiol.* **25**, 818–861.
BARCROFT, J. and BARCROFT, H. (1923). Observations on the taking up of carbon-monoxide by the haemoglobin in the spleen. *J. Physiol.* **58**, 138–144.
BARCROFT, J. and ELLIOT, R. H. E. (1936). Some observations on the denervated spleen. *J. Physiol.* **87**, 189–197.
BARCROFT, J. and FLOREY, H. W. (1928). Some factors involved in the con-centration of blood by the spleen. *J. Physiol.* **66**, 231–234.
— (1929). The effect of exercise on the vascular conditions in the spleen and colon. *J. Physiol.* **68**, 181–189.
BARCROFT, J., HARRIS, H. A., ORAHOVARTS, D. and WEISS, R. (1925). A con-tribution to the physiology of the spleen. *J. Physiol.* **60**, 443–456.
BARCROFT, J., KHANNA, L. C. and NISIMARU, Y. (1932). Rhythmical con-tractions of the spleen. *J. Physiol.* **74**, 294–298.
BARCROFT, J. and NISIMARU, Y. (1932). Cause of rhythmical contraction of the spleen. *J. Physiol.* **74**, 299–310.
BARCROFT, J., NISIMARU, Y. and RAY, G. B. (1932). Observations on the time taken for corpuscles to traverse the liver. *J. Physiol.* **74**, 44–48.
BARCROFT, J. and SHORE, L. E. (1912). The gaseous metabolism of the liver. *J. Physiol.* **45**, 296–306.
BARCROFT, J. and STEPHENS, J. G. (1927). Observations upon the size of the spleen. *J. Physiol.* **64**, 1–22.
BARLOW, T. E. (1951). Arterio-venous anastomoses in the human stomach. *J. Anat.* **85**, 1–5.
BARLOW, T. E., BENTLEY, F. H. and WALDER, D. N. (1951). Arteries, veins and arterio-venous anastomoses in the human stomach. *Surg. Gynec. Obstet.* **93**, 657–671.
BAUER, W., DALE, H. H., POULSSON, L. T. and RICHARDS, D. W. (1932). The control of circulation through the liver. *J. Physiol.* **74**, 343–375.
BAYER, G. O. and SCHER, A. M. (1960). Significance of mesenteric arterial receptors in the reflex regulation of systemic blood pressure. *Circulation Res.* **8**, 845–848.

BAYLISS, L. E. (1952). In *Deformation and Flow in Biological Systems.* Chapter VI. Ed. Frey-Wyssling, A. Amsterdam: North Holland Publishing Co.

BAYLISS, W. M. (1893). On the physiology of the depressor nerve. *J. Physiol.* **14**, 303–325.

— (1902). On the local reactions of the arterial wall to changes in internal pressure. *J. Physiol.* **28**, 220–231.

— (1923). *The Vasomotor System.* London: Longmans.

BAYLISS, W. M. and STARLING, E. H. (1894*a*). Observations on venous pressures and their relationship to capillary pressures. *J. Physiol.* **16**, 159–202.

— (1894*b*). On the origins from the spinal cord of the vaso-constrictor nerves of the portal vein. *J. Physiol.* **17**, 120–128.

— (1899). The movements and innervation of the small intestine. *J. Physiol.* **24**, 99–143.

BEAN, S. W. and SIDKY, M. M. (1957). Effects of low O_2 in intestinal blood flow; tonus and motility. *Amer. J. Physiol.* **189**, 541–554.

BEARN, A. G., BILLING, B., EDHOLM, O. G. and SHERLOCK, S. (1951). Hepatic blood flow and carbohydrate changes in man during fainting. *J. Physiol.* **115**, 442–455.

BEARN, A. G., BILLING, B. and SHERLOCK, S. (1951). The effect of adrenaline and noradrenaline on hepatic blood flow and splanchnic carbohydrate metabolism in man. *J. Physiol.* **115**, 430–441.

— (1952). The response of the liver to insulin in normal subjects and in diabetes mellitus: hepatic vein catheterization studies. *Clin. Sci.* **11**, 151–165.

BEAUMONT, W. (1847). *The Physiology of Digestion.* 2nd ed. Burlington.

BELLMAN, S., LAMBERT, P. B. and FINE, J. (1962). Microscopic observations of the mesenteric circulation in rabbits subjected to reversible and irreversible haemorrhagic shock. In *Shock.* Ciba Foundation Symposium. pp. 96–98. Berlin: Springer-Verlag.

BERNTHAL, T. and SCHWIND, F. J. (1945). Chemoreflex vascular reactions in leg and intestine. *Amer. J. Physiol.* **143**, 361–372.

BILL, A. (1962). Studies of the heated thermocouple principles for determinations of blood flow in tissues. *Acta physiol. scand.* **55**, 111–126.

BILLINGTON, B. P., PATON, A., REYNOLDS, T. B. and SHERLOCK, S. (1954). The effect of hexamethonium bromide on the circulatory and metabolic response to insulin hypoglycaemia in man. *J. Lab. clin. Med.* **43**, 880–887.

BILLROTH, T. (1862). Neue Beitrage zur vergleichenden Anatomie der Milz. *Z. wiss. Zool.* **11**, 325–340.

BIRNIE, J. H. and GRAYSON, J. (1952). Observations on temperature distribution and liver blood flow in the rat. *J. Physiol.* **116**, 189–201.

BISGARD, J. D. and NYE, D. (1940). The influence of hot and cold applications upon gastric and intestinal motor activity. *Surg. Gynec. Obstet.* **71**, 172–180.

BLALOCK, A. and LEVY, S. E. (1937). The effect of haemorrhage, intestinal trauma and histamine on the partition of the blood stream. *Amer. J. Physiol.* **118**, 734–738.

BLALOCK, A. and MASON, M. F. (1936). Observations on the blood flow and gaseous metabolism of the liver of the unanaesthetized dog. *Amer. J. Physiol.* **117**, 328–334.

BLATTBERG, B., MALDONADO, C. and LEVY, M. N. (1960). Intestinal perfusion in haemorrhagic shock. *Circulation Res.* **8**, 920–923.

BLOCH, E. H. (1940). Some actions of adrenalin chloride and acetyl-meta-methylcholine chloride on finer vessels lining frog liver lobules. *Anat. Rec.* 76, Suppl. 2, 7.

BOER, S. DE and CARROL, D. C. (1924a). The mechanism of the splenic reaction to general CO poisoning. *J. Physiol.* 59, 312–332.

— (1924b). The significance of the action of Pituitrin on the splenic volume. *J. Physiol.* 59, 381–386.

BOULTER, P. S. and PARKS, A. G. (1959). Submucosal vascular patterns of the alimentary tract and their significance. *Brit. J. Surg.* 47, 546–550.

BRADFORD, J. R. (1889). The innervation of the renal blood vessels. *J. Physiol.* 10, 358–406.

BRADLEY, S. E. (1949). Variations in hepatic blood flow in man during health and disease. *New Engl. J. Med.* 240, 456–461.

— (1958). Methods for Evaluation of the Splanchnic Circulation. In *Circulation, Proceedings of the Harvey Tercentenary Congress*, pp. 355–365. Oxford: Blackwell Scientific Publications.

BRADLEY, S. E. and INGLEFINGER, F. J. (1952). Determinants of hepatic haemodynamics. In *Visceral Circulation*. Ciba Foundation Symposium. pp. 219–229. London: Churchill.

BRADLEY, S. E., INGLEFINGER, F. J. and BRADLEY, G. P. (1952). Hepatic circulation in cirrhosis of the liver. *Circulation*. 5, 419–429.

BRADLEY, S. E., INGLEFINGER, F. J., BRADLEY, G. P. and CURRY, J. J. (1945). The estimation of hepatic blood flow in man. *J. clin. Invest.* 24, 890–897.

BRADLEY, S. E., MARKS, P. A., REYNELL, P. C. and MELTZER, J. (1953). The circulating splanchnic blood volume in dog and man. *Trans. Assoc. Amer. Physic.* 66, 294–302.

BRANDT, J. L., CASTLEMAN, L., GREENWALD, J. and KELLY, J. (1954). The effect of oral feedings on splanchnic blood flow and oxygen consumption in normals and in subjects with hepatic cirrhosis. *J. clin. Invest.* 33, 919.

BRAUCH, F. (1934). Carotissinusentlastung und Blützuckerspiegel. *Arch. exp. Path. Pharmak.* 175, 104–112.

BRAUER, R. W. (1958). Blood flow distribution in the liver and the circulatory control of liver function. In *Liver Function*. Ed. Brauer, R. W. Amer. Inst. Biol. Sci. Monograph No. 4, 113–127.

BRAUER, R. W., LEONG, G. F., MCELROY, R. E. and HOLLOWAY, R. J. (1955). Haemodynamics of the vascular tree of the isolated rat liver preparation. *Amer. J. Physiol.* 186, 537–542.

BRAUER, R. W. and PRESCOTT, R. C. (1950). Hepatic uptake and biliary excretion of bromsulphalein in the dog. *Amer. J. Physiol.* 162, 565–574.

BROCKISS, J. G. and MOFFATT, D. B. (1958). The intrinsic blood vessels of the pelvic colon. *J. Anat.* 92, 52–56.

BRODIE, T. G. and DIXON, W. E. (1904). Contributions to the physiology of the lungs. Part II. On the innervation in the pulmonary blood vessels and some observations on the action of suprarenal extract. *J. Physiol.* 30, 476–502.

BRUNER, H. D. (1948). Bubble Flow Meter. *Methods med. Res.* 1, 80.

BÜLBRING, E. and BURN, J. H. (1936). Sympathetic vasodilatation in skin and intestine of the dog. *J. Physiol.* 87, 254 274.

BULGAK, A. (1877). Ueber die Contractionen und die Innervation der Milz. *Virchows Arch.* 69, 181–213.

BUNCH, J. L. (1899). On the vasomotor nerves of the small intestine. *J. Physiol.* 24, 72–98.

BURKLE, J. S. and GLIEDMAN, M. L. (1959). External recording method for estimating hepatic blood flow with the use of radio-gold. *Gastro-enterology*. **36**, 112–119.

BURN, J. H. and HUTCHEON, D. E. (1949). The action of noradrenaline. *Brit. J. Pharmacol*. **4**, 373–380.

BURTON, A. C. (1951). On the physical equilibrium of small blood vessels. *Amer. J. Physiol*. **164**, 319–329.

— (1952). Laws of physics and flow in blood vessels. *The Visceral Circulation*. Ciba Foundation Symposium. pp. 70–80. London: Churchill.

— (1959). In *Pulmonary Circulation*. p. 27. Ed. Adams, W. R. and Veith. I. New York: Grune & Stratton.

BURTON-OPITZ, R. (1908*a*). Uber die stromung des Blutes in dem Gebiete der Pfortader. I. Das Stromvolum der Vena Mesenterica. *Arch. fur. ges. Physiol*. **124**, 469–510.

— (1908*b*). Uber die stromung des Blutes in dem Gebiete der Pfortader. II. Das Stromvolum der vena lienalis. *Arch. fur. ges. Physiol*. **129**, 189–216.

— (1910*a*). Uber die stromung des Blutes in dem Gebiete der Pfortader. III. Das stromvolum der vena gastrica. *Arch. fur. ges. Physiol*. **135**, 305–344.

— (1910*b*). Uber die stromung des Blutes in dem Gebiete der Pfortader. IV. Der Einfluss des Plexus mesentericus auf das stromvolumen der vena Mesenterica. *Arch. fur. ges. Physiol*. **135**, 245–248.

— (1911). The vascularity of the liver. II. The influence of the portal blood flow upon the flow in the hepatic artery. *Quart. J. exp. Physiol*. **4**, 93–102; The vascularity of the liver. III. The effect of stimulation of the hepatic plexus upon the flow in the hepatic artery. *Ibid*., **4**, 103–111; The vascularity of the liver. IV. The magnitude of portal inflow. *Ibid*., **4**, 113–125.

— (1912). The vascularity of the liver. V. The influence of the greater splanchnic nerves on arterial inflow. *Quart. J. exp. Physiol*. **5**, 83–90; The vascularity of the liver. VI. The influence of the greater splanchnic nerves on venous inflow. *Ibid*., **5**, 189–196; The vascularity of the liver. VII. The effects of afferent impulses from the hepatic plexus upon the arterial inflow. *Ibid*., **5**, 197–201; The vascularity of the liver. VIII. Influence of adrenaline upon arterial inflow. *Ibid*., **5**, 309–324.

CAESAR, J., SHALDON, S., CHIANDUSSI, L., GUEVARA, L. and SHERLOCK, S. (1961). The use of indocyanine Green in the measurement of hepatic blood flow and as a test of hepatic function. *Clin. Sci*. **21**, 43–57.

CAMERON, G. R. and MAYES, B. T. (1930). Ligation of the hepatic artery. *J. Path. Bact*. **33**, 799–831.

CARLSLAW, H. S. (1921). *The Mathematical Theory of the Conduction of Heat in Solids*. London: Macmillan.

CARLYLE, A. and GRAYSON, J. (1956). Factors involved in the control of cerebral blood flow. *J. Physiol*. **133**, 10–30.

CASSELMAN, W. G. B. and RAPPAPORT, A. M. (1954). "Guided" catheterization of hepatic veins and estimation of hepatic blood flow by the bromsulphalein method in normal dogs. *J. Physiol*. **124**, 173–182.

CELANDER, O. (1954). The range of control exercised by the sympathico-adrenal system. *Acta physiol. scand*. **32**, Suppl. 116, 1–132.

CHAKRAVATI, M. and TRIPOD, J. (1940). The action in the perfused liver of acetylcholine, sympathomimetic substances and local anaesthetics. *J. Physiol*. **97**, 316–329.

CHAMBERS, R. and ZWEIFACH, B. W. (1944). Topography and function of the mesenteric capillary circulation. *Amer. J. Anat.* **75,** 172–205.

CHANG, H. C. and GADDUM, J. H. (1933). Choline esters in tissue extracts. *J. Physiol.* **79,** 255–285.

CHILD, C. G. (1954). *The Hepatic Circulation and Portal Hypertension.* Philadelphia: London: Saunders.

CLARA, M. (1937). *Die arterio-venosen Anastomosen.* Leipzig: Barth.

CLARK, G. A. (1930). The selective vaso-constrictor action of adrenaline. *J. Physiol.* **69,** 171–184.

— (1934). The vaso-dilator action of adrenaline. *J. Physiol.* **80,** 429–440.

CLARK, R. E. and CLARK, E. L. (1934). Observations on living arteriovenous communications as seen in transparent chambers introduced into the rabbit's ear. *Amer. J. Anat.* **54,** 229–286.

CLELAND, J. G. P. and TAIT, J. (1927). Nervous connections of the mammalian spleen, including an account of certain visceromotor and other abdominal reflexes. *Quart. J. exp. Physiol.* **17,** 179–204.

COBBOLD, A., FOLKOW, B., KJELLMER, I. and MELLANDER, S. (1963). Nervous and local chemical control of pre-capillary sphincters in skeletal muscle as measure by changes in filtration coefficient. *Acta physiol. scand.* **57,** 180–192.

COHN, C., LEVINE, R. and KOLINSKY, M. (1948). Hepatic and peripheral removal rates, in the dog, for intravenously injected bromsulphalein. *Amer. J. Physiol.* **155,** 286–289.

COHN, C., LEVINE, R. and STREICHER, D. (1947). The rate of removal of intravenously injected bromsulphalein by the liver and extra-hepatic tissue of the dog. *Amer. J. Physiol.* **150,** 299–303.

COHN, R. and PARSONS, H. (1950). Relationship of portal hypertension and irreversibility of shock. *Amer. J. Physiol.* **160,** 437–440.

CRISP, E. (1855). *Treatise on the Structure and Use of the Spleen.* pp. 1–198. London: "the Author".

CULBERTSON, J. W., WILKINS, R. W., INGLEFINGER, F. J. and BRADLEY, S. E. (1951). The effect of the upright posture and hepatic blood flow in nomotensive and hypertensive subjects. *J. clin. Invest.* **30,** 305–311.

CULL, T. E., SCIBETTA, M. P. and SELKURT, E. E. (1956). Arterial inflow into the mesenteric and hepatic vascular circuits during hemorrhagic shock. *Amer. J. Physiol.* **185,** 365–371.

CUTTING, W. C., DODDS, E. C., NOBLE, R. L. and WILLIAMS, P. C. (1937). The effect of alterations in blood flow on gastric secretion. *Proc. Roy. Soc.* B, **123,** 39–48.

DALE, H. H. (1910). The action of extracts of the pituitary body. *Biochem. J.* **4,** 427–447.

DALE, H. H. and DUDLEY, H. W. (1929). The presence of histamine and acetylcholine in the spleen of the ox and the horse. *J. Physiol.* **68,** 97–123.

DALE, H. H. and LAIDLAW, P. P. (1910). The physiological action of β-iminazolyl-ethylamine. *J. Physiol.* **41,** 318–344.

DALY, M. DE B. and SCOTT, M. J. (1961). Effects of acetylcholine on volume and vascular resistance in the dog's spleen. *J. Physiol.* **156,** 246–259.

DANIEL, P. M. and PRICHARD, M. M. L. (1951a). Variations in the circulation of the portal venous blood within the liver. *J. Physiol.* **114,** 521–537.

— (1951b). Effects of stimulation of the hepatic nerves and of adrenaline upon the circulation of the portal venous blood within the liver. *J. Physiol.* **114,** 538–548.

DAVIDSON, C. S. GIBBONS, T. B. and FALOON, W. W. (1950). Systemic and portal venous pressure in cirrhosis of the liver. *J. Lab. clin. Med.* **35,** 181–187.

DEAL, C. P. and GREEN, H. D. (1956). Comparison of changes in mesenteric resistance following splanchnic nerve stimulation with responses to epinephrine and nor-epinephrine. *Circulation Res.* **4**, 38–44.

DE BUSSCHER, G. (1948). Les anastomoses arterio-veineuses de l'estomac. *Acta Ned. Morph.* **6**, Nos. 1–2, 87–105.

DELORME, E. J., MACPHERSON, A. I. S., MUKHERJEE, S. R. and ROWLANDS, S. (1951). Measurement of the visceral blood volume in dogs. *Quart. J. exp. Physiol.* **36**, 219–231.

DEYSACH, L. J. (1941). Nature and location of "sphincter mechanism" in liver as determined by drug actions and vascular injections. *Amer. J. Physiol.* **132**, 713–724.

DISSE, J. (1890). Uber die Lymphbahnen die Säugethier leber. *Arch. mikr. Anat.* **36**, 203–224.

DOBSON, E. L. and JONES, M. B. (1952). The behaviour of intravenously injected particulate material; its rate of disappearance from the blood stream as a measure of liver blood flow. *Acta med. scand.* **144**, Suppl., 273.

DOBSON, W. (1830). An experimental inquiry into the structure and functions of the spleen. Critical review in *London Med. Physiol. J.* **64**, 356–360.

DOSEKUN, F. O., GRAYSON, J. and MENDEL, D. (1960). The measurement of metabolic and vascular responses in liver and muscle with observations on their responses to insulin and glucose. *J. Physiol.* **150**, 581–606.

DOUGLASS, B. E., BAGGENSTROSS, A. H. and HOLLINSHEAD, W. H. (1950). The anatomy of the portal vein and its tributaries. *Surg. Gynec. Obstet.* **91**, 562–575.

DRIVER, R. L. and VOGT, M. (1950). Carotid sinus reflex and activation of the spleen. *Brit. J. Pharmacol.* **5**, 505–509.

DRURY, A. N., FLOREY, H. and FLOREY, M. E. (1929). The vascular reactions of the colonic mucosa of the dog to fright. *J. Physiol.* **68**, 173–180.

EBERT, R. V. and STEAD, E. A. (1941). Demonstration that in normal man no reserves of blood are mobilized by exercise, epinephrine and haemorrhage. *Amer. J. med. Sci.* **201**, 655–664.

EDHOLM, O. G. (1942). Splanchnic circulation during changes in posture. *J. Physiol.* **101**, 1–10.

EDWARDS, E. A. (1951). Functional anatomy of the portal–systemic communications. *Arch. intern. Med.* **88**, 137–154.

ELIAS, H. (1949a). A re-examination of the structure of the mammalian liver, I. Parenchymal architecture. *Amer. J. Anat.* **84**, 311–327.

— (1949b). A re-examination of the structure of the mammalian liver, II. The hepatic lobule and its relation to the vascular and biliary systems. *Amer. J. Anat.* **85**, 379–456.

— (1953). Observations on the general and regional anatomy of the human liver. *Anat. Rec.* **117**, 377–394.

ELIAS, H. and FELLER, A. (1931). Ueber einen muskulären Drosselmechanismus an den Lebervenenmündungen. *Z. ges. exp. Med.* **77**, 538–550.

ERLANGER, J. and GASSER, H. S. (1919). Studies in secondary traumatic shock. II. Shock due to mechanical limitations of blood flow. *Amer. J. Physiol.* **49**, 151–173.

EULER, U. S. and LILJESTRAND, G. (1935). Einwirkung der sinusentlastung auf Adrenalin, Zucker und Kalzinmgehalt des Blutes, sowie auf den Sauerstoffverbrauch beim Hunde. *Skand. Arch. Physiol.* **71**, 73–84.

EVRINGHAM, A., BRENNEMAN, E. M. and HORVATH, S. M. (1959). Influence of sodium pentothal on splanchnic blood flow and related functions. *Amer. J. Physiol.* **197,** 624–630.

FABER, S. (1936). The action of acetylcholine on the volume of the spleen. *Arch. int. Pharmacodyn.* **53,** 367–376.

FERGUSON, J., IVY, A. C. and GREENGARD, H. (1936). Observations on the response of the spleen to the intravenous injection of certain secretin preparations, acetylcholine and histamine. *Amer. J. Physiol.* **117,** 701–707.

FISCHER, A. and TAKACS, L. (1962). Quoted by Fischer, A. in *The Liver.* Ed. Ch. Rouiller. pp. 329–378. London: Academic Press.

FISCHER, A., TAKACS, L. and MOLNAR, G. (1958). Parallele Bestimmung des arteriellen und portalen Kreislaufs der Leber. *Acta Med. Acad. Sci. Hung.* **12,** 255–264.

FISHER, B., RUSS, C., SELKER, R. G. and FEDOR, E. J. (1956). Observations on liver blood flow. Its relationship to cardiac output in anaesthetized and unanaesthetized animals. *A.M.A. Arch. Surg.* **72,** 600–611.

FOLKOW, B. (1953). A study of factors influencing the tone of denervated blood vessels perfused at various pressures. *Acta physiol. scand.* **27,** 99–177.

FOLKOW, B., FROST, J. and UVNÄS, B. (1948). Action of adrenaline, noradrenaline and some other sympathomimetic drugs on the muscular, cutaneous and splanchnic vessels of the cat. *Acta physiol. scand.* **15,** 412–420.

FOLKOW, B., LEWIS, D. H., LUNDGREN, O., MELLANDER, S. and WALLENTIN, I. (1964a). The effect of graded vasoconstrictor fibre stimulation on the intestinal resistance and capacitance vessels. *Acta physiol. scand.* **61,** 445–457.

FOLKOW, B., LEWIS, D. H., LUNDGREN, O., MELLANDER, S. and WALLENTIN, I. (1964b). The effect of the sympathetic vasoconstrictor fibres on the distribution of capillary blood flow in the intestine. *Acta physiol. scand.* **61,** 458–466.

FOLKOW, B., LUNDGREN, O. and WALLENTIN, I. (1963). Studies on the relationship between flow resistance, capillary filtration coefficient and regional blood volume in the intestine of the cat. *Acta physiol. scand.* **57,** 270–283.

FOLKOW, B. and ÖBERG, B. (1961). Autoregulation and basal tone in consecutive vascular sections of skeletal muscles in reserpine treated cats. *Acta physiol. scand.* **53,** 105–113.

FRANCOIS-FRANCK, C. A. and HALLION, L. (1896a). Recherches expérimentales sur l'innervation vasoconstrictive du foie (1er mémoire: historique et technique). *Arch. Physiol. norm. path.* **8,** 908–922.

— (1896b). Recherches expérimentales sur l'innervation vasoconstrictive du foie (2e mémoire: topographique). *Arch. Physiol. norm. path.* **8,** 923–936.

— (1897a). Recherches expérimentales sur l'innervation vasoconstrictive du foie (3e mémoire: réflexes vaso-constricteurs). *Arch. Physiol. norm. path.* **9,** 434–447.

— (1897b). Recherches expérimentales sur l'innervation vasoconstrictive du foie (4e mémoire: leurs effets mécaniques—leur intervention en présence des poisons traversant le foie). *Arch. Physiol. norm. path.* **9,** 448 458.

FRANK, E. D., FRANK, H. A., JACOB, S., WIEGAL, H. A. E., KORMAN, H. and FINE, J. (1956). Effect of norepinephrine on circulation of the dog in haemorrhagic shock. *Amer. J. Physiol.* **186,** 74–78.

FRANK, H. A., JACOB, S., FRIEDMAN, E. W., RUTENBURG, A. M., GLOTZER, P. and FINE, J. (1952). Traumatic shock; irreversibility of haemorrhagic shock and VDM hypothesis. Failure of ferritin to affect arterial pressure and survival in hepatectomized nephrectomized dogs. *Amer. J. Physiol.* **168**, 150–155.

FRANK, H. A., SELIGMAN, A. M. and FINE, J. (1946). Traumatic shock; prevention of irreversibility in haemorrhagic shock by viviperfusion of liver. *J. clin. Invest.* **25**, 22–29.

FREDERICQ, H. (1929). Le nature parasympathique probable de l'innervation motrice de la rate du chien. *C. R. Soc. Biol., Paris.* **101**, 1164–1165.

FRIEDMAN, E. W., FRANK, H. A. and FINE, J. (1951). Portal circulation in experimental haemorrhagic shock. *Ann. Surg.* **134**, 70–79.

FRIEDMAN, E. W. and WEINER, R. S. (1951). Estimation of hepatic sinusoid pressure by means of venous catheters and estimation of portal pressure by hepatic vein catheterization. *Amer. J. Physiol.* **165**, 527–531.

FRIEDMAN, J. J. (1961). Mesenteric circulation in haemorrhagic shock. *Circulation Res.* **9**, 561–565.

FRIEDMAN, M. H. F. and SNAPE, W. J. (1946). Color changes in the mucosa of the colon in children as affected by food and psychic stimuli. *Fed. Proc.* **5**, 30.

FROHLICH, E. D. and GILLENWATER, J. Y. (1963). Pressure–flow relationships in the perfused dog spleen. *Amer. J. Physiol.* **204**, 645–648.

GALINDO, B. and FREEMAN, J. A. (1963). Fine structure of splenic pulp. *Anat. Rec.* **147**, 25–42.

GAMMON, G. D. and BRONK, D. W. (1935). The discharge of impulses from paccinian corpuscles in the mesentery and its related vascular changes. *Amer. J. Physiol.* **114**, 77–84.

GEBER, W. F. (1960). Quantitative measurement of blood flow in various areas of small and large intestine. *Amer. J. Physiol.* **198**, 985–986.

GIBBS, F. A. (1933). A thermoelectric blood flow recorder in the form of a needle. *Proc. Soc. exp. Biol. N.Y.* **31**, 141–146.

GILMORE, J. P. (1958). Response of estimated hepatic blood flow to graded haemorrhage and the infusion of levarterenol. *Amer. J. Physiol.* **195**, 469–472.

GINSBURG, H. and GRAYSON, J. (1954). Factors controlling liver blood flow in the rat. *J. Physiol.* **123**, 574–602.

GLASER, W. (1928). Uber die motorische Innervierung der Blutgefasse der Milz. Nebst BemerKungen zur intramuralen nervenversorgung der Blutgefasse im Knockenmark. *Z. ges. Anat.* **87**, 741–745.

GOLLWITZER-MEIER, K. (1930). Investigations on the changes of the venous reflux produced by adrenaline. *Z. ges. exp. Med.* **80**, 36–52.

GOLLWITZER-MEIER, K. and ECKHARDT, P. (1934). Ueber die Bedeutung von Hirngefässreflexen fur die Hirndurchblutung. *Arch. exp. Path. Pharmak.* **175**, 689–696.

GOLLWITZER-MEIER, K. and SCHULTE, H. (1931). Der Einfluss der Sinusnerven auf venensystem und Herzminuten volumen. *Arch. fur. ges. Physiol.* **229**, 264–277.

GOTSEV, T. (1936). Uber die Wirkung des Acetylcholine auf Blutgefabe, Blutdruck, Herz und Vasomotorenzentren. *Arch. exp. Path. Pharmak.* **181**, 207–214.

— (1940). Die Bedeutung der Blutgefässe und des Herzens fur die Regulierung des Blutdruckes. *Arch. exp. Physiol.* **195**, 26–42.

GOURIZ, J. T. and NICKERSON, M. (1960). Rubidium 86 uptake by regional vascular beds of the dog during haemorrhagic shock. *The Pharmacologist.* **2**, 73.

GRAB, W., JANSSEN, S. and REIN, H. (1929). Die Leber Als Blutdepot. Klin. *Wschr.* **8**, 1539.

— (1929). Ueber die Grösse der Leberdurchblutung. *Z. Biol.* **89**, 324–331.

GRABNER, G. and NEUMAYR, A. (1958). A continuous recording method for the estimation of liver blood flow in man. In *Circulation. Proceedings of the Harvey Tercentenary Congress.* 386–392. Oxford: Blackwell Scientific Publications.

GRAF, K., GOLENHOFEN, K. and HENSEL, H. (1957). Fortlaufende Registrierung der Leberdurchblutung mit der Wärmeleitsonde. *Pflug. Arch. ges. Physiol.* **264**, 44–60.

GRAF, K. and ROSELL, S. (1958). Untersuchungen zur fortlaufenden Durchblutungsregistrierung mit Warmeleitsonden. *Acta physiol. scand.* **42**, 51–73.

GRANAAT, D. (1953). The spleen in the regulation of arterial blood pressure. *J. Physiol.* **122**, 209–219.

GRANT, R. T. and BLAND, E. F. (1931). Observations on arterio-venous anastomoses in human skin and in the bird's foot with special reference to the reaction to cold. *Heart.* **15**, 385–411.

GRAY, H. (1854). *On the Structure and Use of the Spleen.* London: J. W. Parke.

Gray's Anatomy (1944). Ed. Johnston, T. B. and Whillis, J. 28th Ed. London: Longmans Green.

GRAYSON, J. (1949a). Vascular reactions in the human intestine. *J. Physiol.* **109**, 439–447.

— (1949b). Reactions of the peripheral circulation to external heat. *J. Physiol.* **109**, 53–63.

— (1950). Observations of blood flow in human intestine. *Brit. med. J.* **2**, 1465–1470.

— (1951a). The measurement of intestinal blood flow in man. *J. Physiol.* **114**, 419–434.

— (1951b). Observations on the temperature of the human rectum. *Brit. med. J.* **2**, 1379–1382.

— (1951c). Cold and warmth vasoconstrictor responses in the skin of man. *Brit. Heart J.* **13**, 167–176.

— (1952). Internal calorimetry in the determination of thermal conductivity and blood flow. *J. Physiol.* **118**, 54–72.

— (1954). The role of the portal vein in the integration of splanchnic blood flow. *L'Hypertension portale. Le "Dumping syndrome".* IVᵉ *Congrès de Gastro-Entérologie.* pp. 1–26. Paris: Masson.

GRAYSON, J. and JOHNSON, D. H. (1953). The effect of adrenaline and noradrenaline on the liver blood flow. *J. Physiol.* **120**, 73–94.

GRAYSON, J. and KINNEAR, T. (1958). Vascular and metabolic responses of the liver to insulin. *J. Physiol.* **144**, 52–67.

— (1962). Observations on temperature, blood flow and heat production in the human liver in relation to environment and to glucose and insulin administration. *Clin. Sci.* **22**, 125–140.

GRAYSON, J. and MENDEL, D. (1956). The distribution and regulation of temperature in the rat. *J. Physiol.* **133**, 334–346.

— (1957a). The role of the spleen and hepatic artery in the regulation of liver blood flow. *J. Physiol.* **136**, 60–79.

— (1957b). Observations on the intrahepatic flow interactions of the hepatic artery and portal vein. *J. Physiol.* **139**, 167–177.

GRAYSON, J. and SWAN, H. J. C. (1950a). Action of adrenaline, noradrenaline and dihydroergocarmine in the colonic circulation. *Lancet*, **252**, 488–490.

GRAYSON, J. and SWAN, H. J. C. (1950b). Intestinal blood flow changes in men during fainting. *J. Physiol.* **112**, 44P.

GREEN, H. D. (1962). Physiology of peripheral circulation in shock. *Fed. Proc.* **20**, 61–68. Conference on Shock.

GREEN, H. D., DEAL, C. P., BARDHANABAEDYA, S. and DENISON, A. B. (1955). The effect of adrenergic substances and ischaemia on the blood flow and peripheral resistance of the canine mesenteric vascular bed before and during adrenergic blockade. *J. Pharmacol.* **113**, 115–123.

GREEN, H. D. and KEPCHAR, J. H. (1959). Control of peripheral resistance in major systemic vascular beds. *Physiol. Rev.* **39**, 617–686.

GREEN, H. D., LOCKSLEY, S. H., HALL, S. L., SEXTON, J. and DEAL, C. P. (1959). Autonomic vasomotor responses in the canine hepatic arterial and venous beds. *Amer. J. Physiol.* **196**, 196–206.

GREEN, H. D., OTTIS, K. and KITCHEN, T. (1960). Autonomic stimulation and blockade in canine splenic inflow, outflow and weight. *Amer. J. Physiol.* **198**, 424–428.

GREGG, D. E. (1962). Haemodynamic factors in shock. In *Shock.* Ciba Foundation Symposium. pp. 50–60. Berlin: Springer-Verlag.

GRIFFITH, F. R. and EMERY, F. E. (1930). The vasomotor control of the liver circulation. *Amer. J. Physiol.* **95**, 20–34.

GRIM, E. and LINDSETH, E. O. (1958). Distribution of blood flow to the tissues of the small intestine of the dog. *Minn. Med.* **30**, 138–145.

GRINDLAY, J. H., HERRICK, J. F. and BALDES, E. J. (1939). Rhythmicity of the spleen in relation to blood flow. *Amer. J. Physiol.* **127**, 119–126.

GRINDLAY, J. H., HERRICK, J. F. and MANN, F. C. (1939). Measurement of the blood flow of the spleen. *Amer. J. Physiol.* **127**, 106–118.

— (1941). Measurement of blood flow of the liver. *Amer. J. Physiol.* **132**, 489–496.

GRODINS, F. S., OSBORNE, S. L., IVY, A. C. and GOLDMAN, L. (1941). The effect of bile acids on hepatic blood flow. *Amer. J. Physiol.* **132**, 375–389.

HALE, A. J. (1951). The minute structure of the liver; A review. *Glasgow. med. J.* **32**, 283–301.

HALLION, L. and FRANCOIS-FRANCK, C. A. (1896). Recherches expérimentales exécutées à l'aide d'un nouvel appareil volumétrique sur l'innervation vaso-motrice de l'intestin. *Arch. de Physiol.* **8**, 478–492.

HAMRICK, L. W. (JR.) and MYERS, J. D. (1955). The effect of haemorrhage on hepatic blood flow and splanchnic oxygen consumption of the dog. *Circulation Res.* **3**, 65–72.

HANAK, A. and HARKAVY, J. (1924). Observations on the taking up of carbon-monoxide by the haemoglobin of the spleen. *J. Physiol.* **59**, 121–128.

HARGIS, E. H. and MANN, F. C. (1925). A plethysmographic study of the changes in the volume of the spleen in the intact animal. *Amer. J. Physiol.* **75**, 180–200.

HAUSNER, E., ESSEX, H. E. and MANN, F. C. (1938). Roentgenologic observations on the spleen of the dog under ether, sodium amytal, pentobarbital sodium and pentothal sodium anaesthesia. *Amer. J. Physiol.* **121**, 387–391.

HAYNES, R. H. and BURTON, A. C. (1959). Role of non-Newtonian behaviour of blood in haemodynamics. *Amer. J. Physiol.* **197**, 943–950.

HEINEMANN, H. O., SMYTHE, C. M. and MARKS, P. A. (1953). Effect of haemorrhage on estimated hepatic blood flow and renal blood flow in dogs. *Amer. J. Physiol.* **174**, 352–356.

HENDERSON, Y. (1910). Acapnia and shock. VII. Failure of the circulation. *Amer. J. Physiol.* **27**, 152–176.

HENLE, J. (1852). Versuche und Beobachtungen an einem Enthaupteten. *Z. Rat. Med. N.F.* **2**, 299–312.

HENSEL, H., RUEF, J. and GOLENHOFEN, K. (1954). Fortlaufende Registrierung der Muskeldurchblutung am Menschen mit einer Calorimetersonde. *Pflug. Arch. ges. Physiol.* **259**, 267–280.

HERRICK, J. F., GRINDLAY, J. H., BALDES, E. J. and MANN, F. C. (1940). Effect of exercise on the blood flow in the superior mesenteric renal and common iliac arteries. *Amer. J. Physiol.* **128**, 338–344.

HERRICK, J. F., MANN, F. C., ESSEX, H. E. and BALDES, E. J. (1934). Effect of digestion of food on the blood flow from the liver of the dog. *Amer. J. Physiol.* **109**, 52P.

HEYMANS, C. (1929). Le sinus carotidien, Zone réflexogène régulatione du tonus vagal cardiaque du tonus neurovasculaire et de l'adrenalin-sécrétion. *Arch. int. Pharmacodyn.* **35**, 269–306.

HEYMANS, C., BOUCKAERT, J. J. and DAUTRELBE., L. (1930). Sinus carotidien et réflexes venomoteurs mesenterique. *C. R. Soc. Biol., Paris,* **105**, 217–219.

HEYMANS, C., DE SCHAEPDRYVER, A. F. and DE VLEESCHHOUWER, G. R. (1960). Abdominal baro and chemo sensitivity in dogs. *Circulation Res.* **8**, 347–352.

HILL, L. (1895). The influence of the force of gravity on the circulation of the blood. *J. Physiol.* **18**, 15–53.

HJORTSÖ, C. H. (1951). The topography of the intrahepatic duct systems. *Acta anat.* **11**, 599–615.

HOLTZ, P., BACHMANN, F., ENGLEHARDT, A. and GREEFF, K. (1952). Die Milzwirkung des Adrenalins und Arterenols. *Arch. fur. ges. Physiol.* **255**, 232–250.

HOLTZ, P. and SCHUMANN, H. J. (1949). Karotissinusentlastung und Nebennieren. *Arch. exp. Path. Pharmak.* **206**, 49–64.

HORVATH, S. M., KELLY, T., FOLK, G. E. and HUTT, B. K. (1957). Measurement of blood volumes in the splanchnic bed of the dog. *Amer. J. Physiol.* **189**, 573–575.

HOSKINS, R. G. and GUNNING, R. E. L. (1917). Effects of adrenaline on the distribution of the blood. V. Volume changes and venous discharge in the intestine. *Amer. J. Physiol.* **43**, 399–407.

HUNT, R. (1918). Vasodilator reactions. 1. *Amer. J. Physiol.* **45**, 197–230.

INGLEFINGER, F. J. (1947). Hepatic function with respect to bromsulphalein removal. *Bull. New Engl. Med. Center.* **9**, 25–29.

IRWIN, J. W. and MACDONALD, J. (1953). Microscopic observations of the intrahepatic circulation of living guinea pigs. *Anat. Rec.* **117**, 1–15.

IZQUIERDO, J. J. and CANNON, W. B. (1928). Studies on the conditions of activity in endocrine glands. *Amer. J. Physiol.* **84**, 545–562.

IZQUIERDO, J. J. and KOCH, E. (1930). Ueber den Einfluss der Nern splanchnici auf den arteriellen Blutdruck des Kaninchens. *Z. Kreisl-Forsch.* **22**, 735–743.

JARISCH, A. and LUDWIG, W. (1926). Influence of N. depressor with special reference to participation of heart. *Arch. exp. Path. Pharmak.* **114**, 240–251.

JEFFERSON, N. C., PROFFITT, M. M. and NECHELES, H. (1952). Collateral arterial circulation to the liver of the dog. *Surgery.* **31**, 724–730.

JOHNSON, D. H. (1953). *The Liver in Hypotension.* M.D. Thesis. University of Bristol.

— (1954). The effect of haemorrhage and hypertension on the liver blood flow. *J. Physiol.* **126**, 413–432.

JOHNSON, D. H., GINSBURG, M. and GRAYSON, J. (1952). The nervous regulation of liver blood flow. *J. Physiol.* **117**, 74P.

JOHNSON, P. C. (1959). Myogenic nature of increase in intestinal vascular resistance with venous pressure elevation. *Circulation Res.* **7**, 992–999.

— (1960). Autoregulation of intestinal blood flow. *Amer. J. Physiol.* **199**, 311–318.

JOHNSON, P. C. and SELKURT, E. E. (1958). Intestinal weight changes in haemorrhagic shock. *Amer. J. Physiol.* **193**, 135–143.

JOHNSON, R. H. (1964). Some vasomotor changes in temperature regulation in man. *Proc. 3rd European Conference on Microcirculation.*

KALTREIDER, N. L., MENEELY, G. E. and ALLEN, J. R. (1942). Effect of epinephrine on volume of blood. *J. clin. Invest.* **21**, 339–345.

KATZ, L. N. and RODBARD, S. (1939). The integration of the vaso-motor responses in the liver with those in other systemic vessels. *J. Pharmacol.* **67**, 407–421.

KELAN, M. and ZWEIFACH, B. W. (1954). Influence of partial and complete evisceration on the action of drugs protecting against lethal haemorrhage. *Surg. Gynec. Obstet.* **99**, 707–712.

KETTERER, S. G., WIEGLAND, B. D. and RAPAPORT, E. (1960). Hepatic uptake and biliary excretion of Indocyanine green and its use in estimation of hepatic blood flow in dogs. *Amer. J. Physiol.* **199**, 481–484.

KIERNAN, F. (1833). The anatomy and histology of the liver. *Trans. Roy. Soc. London.* **123**, 711–770.

KIESE, M. and LANGE, G. (1957). Calorimetrische Messung der Durchblutung des Herzmuskels. *Arch. exp. Path. Pharmak.* **231**, 149–157.

KLEMPERER, P. (1938). The Spleen. In *Downey's Handbook of Hematology.* Vol. 3, pp. 1591–1754. New York: Hoeber.

KNISELY, M. H. (1936a). Method of illuminating living structures for microscopic study. *Anat. Rec.* **64**, 499–524.

— (1936b). Spleen studies. 1. Microscopic observations of the circulatory system of living unstimulated mammalian spleens. *Anat. Rec.* **65**, 23–50.

— (1939). Microscopic observations of circulatory conditions in living frog liver lobules. *Anat. Rec.* **73**, 69–70.

KNISELY, M. H., HARDING, F. and DEBACKER, H. (1957). Hepatic sphincters. *Science.* **125**, 1023–1026.

KOCH, E. and NORDMANN, M. (1928). Mikroskopische Kreislauf—beobachtungen in Splanchnikusgebiet des Kaninchens mit gleichzeitiger Blutdruckverzeichnung. *Z. KreislForsch.* **20**, 343–347.

KOLIN, A. (1936). An electromagnetic flowmeter. Principle of the method and its application to blood flow measurements. *Proc. Soc. exp. Biol., N.Y.* **35**, 53–56.

KRAFKA, J., MCCREA, F. D. and VOGT, E. (1929). The activity of the spleen in anaphylactic shock. *J. Physiol.* **68**, 292–294.

KRAMER, K. and LUFT, C. U. (1951). Mobilization of red cells and oxygen from the spleen in severe hypoxia. *Amer. J. Physiol.* **165**, 215–228.

KREBS, J. S. and BRAUER, R. W. (1958). Metabolism of sulfobromopthalein sodium (BSP) in the rat. *Amer. J. Physiol.* **194**, 37–43.

— (1960). Modification of BSP metabolism by bile stasis and liver injury. *Amer. J. Physiol.* **198**, 774–778.

KREMER, M. and WRIGHT, S. (1932). The effects on blood pressure of section of the splanchnic nerves. *Quart. J. exp. Physiol.* **21**, 319–335.

KRETZ, R. (1894). On hypertrophy and regeneration of the liver tissue. *Wien. klin. Wscher.* **7**, 365–368.

KUNTZ, A. and JACOBS, M. W. (1955). Components of periarterial extensions of coeliac and mesenteric plexuses. *Anat. Rec.* **123**, 509–520.

LAPLACE, P. S. (1841). *Mechanique celeste.* Vol. 10.

LATSCHENBERGER, J. and DEAHNA, A. (1876). Beitrage zur Lehre von der reflectorischen Erregung der Gefassmuskeln. *Pflugers. Arch.* **12,** 157–204.

LAWSON, H. and CHUMLEY, J. (1940). The effect of distension on blood flow through the intestine. *Amer. J. Physiol.* **131,** 368–377.

LETNIK-SATYUKOVA, G. S. (1951). The nerves of the arteries of the stomach. Quoted by Grigor-Eva, T. A., in *The Innervation of Blood Vessels,* p. 159. 1962. Oxford: Pergamon Press.

LEVY, N. M. (1958). Influence of levarterenol on portal venous flow in acute haemorrhage. *Circulation Res.* **6,** 587–591.

LEWIS, H. P. (1951). Pain in acute and chronic diseases of the liver. *Ann. intern. Med.* **35,** 878–887.

LEWIS, R. N., WERLE, J. M. and WIGGERS, C. J. (1943). The behaviour of the spleen in haemorrhagic hypotension and shock. *Amer. J. Physiol.* **138,** 205–211.

LINDGREN, P. and UVNÄS, B. (1953). Activation of sympathetic vasodilator and vasoconstrictor neurones by electric stimulation in the medulla of dog and cat. *Circulation Res.* **1,** 479–485.

LINZELL, J. L. (1953). Internal calorimetry in the measurement of blood flow with heated thermocouples. *J. Physiol.* **121,** 390–402.

LIPSCOMB, A. and CRANDALL, L. A. (1947). Hepatic blood flow and glucose output in normal unanaesthetized dogs. *Amer. J. Physiol.* **148,** 302–311.

LOEWE, S. and FAURE, W. (1925). Un mittel barer Nachweiss der Muskeltatigbeit der Milz Kapsel. *Klin. Wschr.* **4,** 1358–1359.

LOFVING, B. and MELLANDER, S. (1955). Quoted by Folkow, B. in *The Control of the Circulation.* Ed. McDowall, R. J. S. p. 21. 1956. London: Dawson.

LONGMIRE, W. P., MULDER, D. G., MAHONEY, P. S. and METHINKOFF, S. W. (1958). Side to side porta caval anastomoses for portal hypertension. *Ann. Surg.* **147,** 881–894.

LUDWIG, C. (1863). Quoted from *Howell's Textbook of Physiology* (1946). p. 660. London: Saunders.

LUDWIG, H. (1932). The function of the blood depot. *Z. ges. exp. Med.* **80,** 36–52.

MCCOMIS, W., CHARM, S. and KURLAND, G. (1964). Pulsating blood flow energy losses in small tubes. *Proc. 3rd European Conference on Microcirculation.*

MCINDOE, A. H. (1928). Vascular lesions of portal cirrhosis. *Arch. Path. (Lab. Med.).* **5,** 23–42.

MACKENZIE, D. W., WHIPPLE, A. O. and WINTERSTEINER, M. P. (1941). Studies on the microscopic anatomy and physiology of living trans-illuminated mammalian spleens. *Amer. J. Anat.* **68,** 397–456.

MCLAUGHLIN, A. R. (1928). The role of the liver in controlling the distribution of blood. *J. Pharmacol.* **34,** 147–168.

MACLEOD, J. J. R. and PEARCE, R. G. (1914). The outflow of blood from the liver as affected by variations in the condition of the portal vein and hepatic artery. *Amer. J. Physiol.* **35,** 87–105.

MCMICHAEL, J. (1932). The portal circulation, I. The action of adrenaline and pituitary pressor extract. *J. Physiol.* **75,** 241 263.

— (1933). The portal circulation, II. The action of acetylcholine. *J. Physiol.* **77,** 399–421.

MACNEAL, W. J. (1929). Circulation of blood through the spleen pulp. *Arch. Path.* **7,** 215–227.

MAEGRAITH, B. G. (1958). Sinusoids and sinusoidal flow. In *Liver Function*. Ed. Brauer, R. W. Washington: Amer. Inst. Biol. Sci. Monograph No. 4, pp. 135–139.

MAGNUS, R. and SCHAFER, E. A. (1901*a*). Does the vagus contain motor fibres for the spleen? *J. Physiol.* **27,** 3P.

— (1901*b*). The action of pituitary extract upon the kidney. *J. Physiol.* **27,** xP.

MALCOLM, J. D. (1910). Discussion of the prevention and treatment of shock. *Brit. med. J.* **2,** 760–761.

MALL, F. P. (1892). Der Einfluss des Systems der Vena Portae auf die Vertheilung des Blutes. *Arch. f. Physiol.* **16,** 409–453.

— (1896). A study of intestinal contraction. *Johns Hopk. Hosp. Rep.* **1,** 37–75.

— (1906). A study of the structural unit of the liver. *Amer. J. Anat.* **5,** 227–308.

MANN, F. C. (1915). Shock and haemorrhage; an experimental study. *Surg. Gynec. Obstet.* **21,** 430–441.

MASUDA, T. (1927). The action of the vagus on the spleen. *J. Physiol.* **62,** 289–300.

MAUTNER, H. (1924). Die Bedeutung der Venen und deren Sperrvorrichtungen fur den Wasseranstalt. *Wien. Arch. inn. Med.* **7,** 251–310.

MAUTNER, H. and PICK, E. P. (1915). Ueber die durch Schockgifte erzeugten Zirkulationsstorungen. *Münch. med. Wschr.* **62,** 1141–1143.

MELLANDER, S. (1960). Comparative studies on the adrenergic neuro-hormonal control of resistance and capacitance blood vessels in the cat. *Acta physiol. scand.* **50,** Suppl. 176.

MERTENS, O. (1935). Die Milz als Kreislauforgan. *Nachr. Ges. Wiss. N.F. Göttingen),* **1,** 261–283.

MICHELS, N. A. (1955). *Blood Supply and Anatomy of the Upper Abdominal Organs.* London: Pitman Med. Pub.

MIKHAIL, Y. and SALEH, A. L. (1961). Intrinsic nerve fibres in the liver parenchyma. *Anat. Rec.* **141,** 317–323.

MITCHELL, G. A. G. (1935). The innervation of the distal colon. *Edinb. med. J.* **42,** 11–20.

— (1940). A macroscopic study of the nerve supply of the stomach. *J. Anat., Lond.* **75,** 50–73.

MOORE, R. D., MUMAW, V. R. and SCHOENBERG, M. D. (1964). The structure of the spleen and its functional implications. *Exp. Molec. Path.* **3,** 31–50.

MYERS, J. D. and HICKAM, E. B. (1948). An estimation of hepatic blood flow and oxygen consumption in heart failure. *J. clin. Invest.* **27,** 620–632.

MYERS, J. D. and TAYLOR, W. J. (1951). An estimation of portal venous pressure by occlusive catheterization of an hepatic venule. *J. clin. Invest.* **30,** 662–663.

NAKATA, K. (1954). Blood stream in the spleen. *Acta haemat.* **11,** 263–268.

NAKATA, K., LEONG, G. F. and BRAUER, R. W. (1960). Direct measurement of blood pressures in minute vessels of the liver. *Amer. J. Physiol.* **199,** 1181–1188.

NECHELES, H., FRANK, R., KAYE, W. and ROSENMAN, E. (1936). Effect of acetylcholine on the blood flow through the stomach and legs of the rat. *Amer. J. Physiol.* **114,** 695–699.

NECHELES, H., LEVITSKY, P., KOHN, P., MASKINS, M. and FRANK, R. (1936). The vasomotor effect of acetylcholine on the stomach of the dog. *Amer. J. Physiol.* **114,** 330–336.

NOER, R. J. (1943). The blood vessels of the jejunum and ileum. A comparative study of man and certain laboratory animals. *Amer. J. Anat.* **73,** 293–334.

NOER, R. J., ROBB, J. H. and JACOBSEN, L. F. (1951). Circulatory disturbances produced by acute intestinal obstruction in the living animal. *A.M.A. Arch. Surg.* **63,** 520–528.

OLDS, J. M. and STAFFORD, E. S. (1930). On the manner of anastomosis of the hepatic and portal circulations. *Johns Hopk. Hosp. Bull.* **47,** 176–184.

OLIVER, G. (1897). The action of animal extracts on the peripheral vessels. *J. Physiol.* **21,** 22P.

OLIVER, G. and SCHAFER, E. A. (1895). The physiological effects of the suprarenal capsules. *J. Physiol.* **18,** 230–276.

OPPENHEIMER, M. J. and MANN, F. C. (1943). Intestinal capillary circulation during distension. *Surgery.* **13,** 548–554.

OTTIS, K., DAVIS, J. E. and GREEN, H. C. (1957). Effects of adrenergic and cholinergic drugs on splenic inflow and outflow before and after adrenergic blockade. *Amer. J. Physiol.* **189,** 599–608.

PAGE, I. H. and ABELL, R. G. (1943). The vessels of the mesentery in shock. *J. exp. Med.* **77,** 215–232.

PARRATT, J. R. and WEST, G. B. (1957). 5-Hydroxytryptamine and tissue mast cells. *J. Physiol.* **137,** 169–178.

PARSON, W., MAYERSON, H. S., LYONS, C., PORTER, B. and TRAUTMAN, W. V. (1948). Effect of the administration of adrenaline on the circulating red cell volume. *Amer. J. Physiol.* **155,** 239–241.

PATON, A., REYNOLDS, T. B. and SHERLOCK, S. (1953). Assessment of portal venous hypertension by catheterization of hepatic veins. *Lancet.* **1,** 918–921.

PATTISON, A. C. (1954). Hepatic vein pressure studies for evaluation of intra hepatic portal hypertension. *A.M.A. Arch. Surg.* **68,** 442–445.

PECK, H. and HOERR, N. L. (1951). The intermediary circulation in the red pulp of the mouse spleen. *Anat. Rec.* **109,** 447–477.

PERL, W. (1962). Heat and matter distribution in body tissues and the determination of tissue blood flow by local clearance method. *J. theoret. Biol.* **2,** 201–235.

POISEUILLE, J. L. M. (1830). Recherches sur les causes du mouvement du sang dans les veines. *J. Physiol. Path. gen.* **10,** 277–295.

POPPER, H. (1931). Ueber Drosselvorrichtungen an Lebervenen. *Berl. klin. Wschr.* **10,** 2129–2131.

PRINZMETAL, M., ORNITZ, E. M., SIMKIN, B. and BERGMAN, H. C. (1948). Arteriovenous anastomoses in liver, spleen and lungs. *Amer. J. Physiol.* **152,** 48–52.

RADOSTINA, T. N. (1953). The control of the blood supply of the intestine. Quoted by Grigor-Eva, T. A., in *Innervation of Blood Vessels,* pp. 212–213. Oxford: Pergamon Press, 1962.

RANSON, S. W. (1935). *The Anatomy of the Nervous System.* 5th Ed. p. 331. London: Saunders.

RANSON, S. W. and BILLINGSLEY, P. R. (1918). Studies on the sympathetic nervous system. *J. comp. Neurol.* **29,** 305–312.

REIN, H. (1928). Die Thermo-stromuhr. Ein Verfahren zur fortlaufenden Messung der mittleren Absoluten durch Flussmengen in uneroffneten Gefassen in situ. *Z. Biol.* **87,** 394–418.

— (1949). Über ein Regulation system "Milz-Leber" fur den oxydatiren stoffwechsel der korpergewebe und besonders des Herzens. *Naturwissenschaften.* **36,** 233–239; 260–268.

REIN, H. (1951). Die Beeinflussung von Coronar-oder Hypoxie—bedingten Myokard—Insuffizienzen durch Milz and Leber. *Arch. fur. ges. Physiol.* **253**, 435–458.

REIN, H. and ROSSLER, R. (1929). Die Abhangigkeit der vasomotorischen Blutdruckregulation bei akuten Blutverlusten von den thermo-regulatorischen Blutverschiebungen in Gesamtkreislaufe. *Z. Biol.* **89**, 237–248.

REYNELL, P. C., MARKS, P. A., CHIDSEY, C. and BRADLEY, S. E. (1955). Changes in splanchnic blood volume and splanchnic blood flow in dogs after haemorrhage. *Clin. Sci.* **14**, 407–419.

RICHINS, C. A. (1948). Use of freeze drying technique for study of vascular activity. *Science*, **107**, 25.

RIEDEL, H. (1932). Gas Gefassystem der Katsenmilz. *Z. Zellforsch.* **15**, 459–529.

RIEGELE, L. (1929). Uber die mikroscopische Innervation der Milz. *Z. Zellforsch.* **9**, 511–533.

ROACH, M. R. and BURTON, A. C. (1957). The reason for the shape of the distensibility curves of arteries. *Canad. J. Biochem. Physiol.* **35**, 681–690.

ROBINSON, W. L. (1926). The vascular mechanism of the spleen. *Amer. J. Path.* **2**, 341–355.

ROUS, P. and GILDING, H. P. (1929). Studies of tissue maintenance. I. The changes with diminished blood bulk. *J. exp. Med.* **50**, 189.

ROY, C. S. (1882). The physiology and pathology of the spleen. *J. Physiol.* **3**, 203–228.

RUTTNER, J. and VOGEL, M. (1957). Elektronenmikroskopische Untersuch-ungen an der Lebersinusoidwand. *Verh. dtsch. Ges. Pathol.* **41**, 314–324.

SAAD, K. (1935). The effects of drugs on the isolated splenic capsule of man and other animals. *Quart. J. Pharm.* **8**, 31–38.

SALMON, P. A., GRIFFEN, W. O. and WANGENSTEEN, O. H. (1959). Effect of intragastric temperature changes upon gastric blood flow. *Proc. Soc. exp. Biol. N.Y.* **101**, 442–444.

SAPIRSTEIN, L. A. (1956). Fractionation of the cardiac output of rats with isotopic potassium. *Circulation Res.* **4**, 689–692.

— (1958a). Regional blood flow by fractional distribution of indicators. *Amer. J. Physiol.* **193**, 161–168.

— (1958b). Indicator distribution methods in the measurement of splanchnic blood flow of the normal dog. In *Liver Function*. Ed. Brauer, R. W. Amer. Inst. Biol. Sci. Monograph No. 4, 93–105.

SAPIRSTEIN, L. A., SAPIRSTEIN, E. H. and BREDEMAYER, A. (1960). The effect of haemorrhage on the cardiac output and its distribution in the rat. *Circulation Res.* **8**, 135–147.

SAPIRSTEIN, L. A. and SIMPSON, A. M. (1955). Plasma clearance of Rose Bengal (tetra iodo tetra brom fluorescein). *Amer. J. Physiol.* **182**, 337–346.

SARNOFF, J. S. and YAMADA, I. S. (1959). Evidence for reflex control of arterial pressures from abdominal receptors with special reference to the pancreas. *Circulation Res.* **7**, 352–355.

SCHAFER, A. E. and MOORE, B. (1896). On the contractility and innervation of the spleen. *J. Physiol.* **20**, 1–50.

SCHIFF, M. (1867). *Leçons sur la physiologie de la digestion*. Florence et Turin: Loescher.

SCHMID, H. E. and SPENCER, M. P. (1962). Characteristics of pressure flow regulation by the kidney. *J. appl. Physiol.* **17**, 201–204.

SCHMID, J. (1908). Die grosse des Blutstroms in der Pfortader. *Arch. fur. ges. Physiol.* **125,** 527–540.

— (1909). Beeinflussung von Druck und Stromvolumen in der Pfortader durch die Atmung and durch experimentalle Eingriffe. *Pflug. Arch.* **126,** 165–196.

SCHMIDT, C. F. and PIERSON, J. C. (1934). The intrinsic regulation of the blood vessels of the medulla oblongata. *Amer. J. Physiol.* **108,** 241–263.

SCHUMACHER, S. (1938). Ueber die Bedeutung der arterio-venosen Anastomosen und der epithelioiden Muskelzellen (Quellzellen). *Z. mikr.-anat. Forsch.* **43,** 107–130.

SCHWEIGGER-SEIDEL, F. (1863). Untersuchunggen uber die Milz. *Arch. path. Anat.* **27,** 460–504.

SCHWIEGK, H. (1932). Untersuchungen uber die Leberdurchblutung und den Pfortaderkreislauf. *Arch. exp. Path. Pharmak.* **168,** 693–714.

SEGALL, H. (1923). An experimental investigation of blood and bile channels of the liver. *Surg. Gynec. Obstet.* **37,** 152–178.

SELKURT, E. E. (1948). Measurement of renal blood flow. *Methods med. Res.* **1,** 191.

— (1953). Validity of the Bromsulphalein (BSP) method for estimating hepatic blood flow. *Amer. J. Physiol.* **175,** 461–467.

— (1959). Intestinal ischaemic shock and the protective role of the liver. *Amer. J. Physiol.* **197,** 281–285.

SELKURT, E. E., ALEXANDER, R. S. and PATTERSON, M. B. (1947). The role of the mesenteric circulation in the irreversibility in haemorrhagic shock. *Amer. J. Physiol.* **149,** 732–743.

SELKURT, E. E. and BRECHER, G. A. (1956). Splanchnic haemodynamics and oxygen utilization during haemorrhagic shock in the dog. *Circulation Res.* **4,** 693–704.

SELKURT, E. E. and JOHNSON, P. C. (1958). Effect of acute elevation of portal venous pressure on mesenteric blood volume, interstitial fluid volume and haemodynamics. *Circulation Res.* **6,** 592–599.

SELKURT, E. E. and ROTHE, C. F. (1960). Splanchnic baroreceptors in the dog. *Amer. J. Physiol.* **199,** 335–340.

— (1962). Critical analysis of experimental haemorrhagic shock in animals. Fed. Proc. 20. Conference on Shock. 30–37.

SELKURT, E. E., SCIBETTA, M. P. and CULL, T. E. (1958). Haemodynamics of intestinal circulation. *Circulation Res.* **6,** 92–99.

SENEVIRATNE, R. D. (1949). Physiological and pathological responses in the blood vessels of the liver. *Quart. J. exp. Physiol.* **35,** 77–110.

SHACKMAN, R., GRABER, I. G. and MELROSE, D. G. (1953). Liver blood flow and general anaesthesia. *Clin. Sci.* **12,** 307–318.

SHALDON, C. (1960). Recording venous pressure in man. *Lancet,* **2,** 244.

SHALDON, C., PEACOCK, J. H., WALKER, R. M., PALMER, D. B. and BADRICK, F. E. (1961). The portal venous content of adrenaline and noradrenaline in portal hypertension. *Lancet,* **1,** 957–961.

SHALDON, S., CHIANDUSI, L., GUEVERA, L., CAESAR, T. and SHERLOCK, S. (1961). The estimation of hepatic blood flow and intra-hepatic shunted blood by colloidal heat-denatured human serum albumen labelled with I^{131}. *J. clin. Invest.* **40,** 1346 1351

SHERLOCK, S., BEARN, A. G., BILLING, B. H. and PATERSON, J. C. S. (1950). Splanchnic blood flow in man by bromsulphalein method—the relation of peripheral plasma bromsulphalein levels to the calculated flow. *J. Lab. clin. Med.* **35,** 923–932.

SHIPLEY, R. E., GREGG, D. E. and WEARN, J. T. (1942). Operative mechanism of some errors in the application of the thermostromuhr method to the measurement of blood flow. *Amer. J. Physiol.* **136**, 263–274.

SHIPLEY, R. E. and STUDY, R. S. (1951). Changes in renal blood flow, extraction of inulin, glomerular filtration rate, tissue pressure and urine flow with acute alterations of renal artery blood pressure. *Amer. J. Physiol.* **167**, 676–688.

SHIPLEY, R. E. and WILSON, C. (1951). An improved recording rotameter. *Proc. Soc. exp. Biol.*, *N.Y.*, **78**, 724–728.

SHOEMAKER, W. G., VAN ITALLIE, T. B. and WALKER, W. F. (1959). Measurement of hepatic glucose output and hepatic blood flow in response to glucagon. *Amer. J. Physiol.* **196**, 315–318.

SHORR, E., ZWEIFACH, B. W. and FURCHGOTT, R. F. (1945). On the occurrence, sites and modes of origin and destruction of principles affecting the compensatory vascular mechanism in experimental shock. *Science.* **102**, 489–498.

SHOSKES, M. (1948). Responses of colonic muscle to local application of drugs. *Gastroenterology.* **10**, 305–309.

SIDKY, M. and BEAN, J. W. (1958). Influence of rhythmic and tonic contraction of intestinal muscle on blood flow and blood reservoir capacity in dog intestine. *Amer. J. Physiol.* **193**, 386–392.

SIMONDS, J. P. (1923). A study of the simultaneous changes in blood pressure in the carotid artery and jugular and portal veins in anaphylactic and peptone shock in the dog. *Amer. J. Physiol.* **65**, 512–526.

SIMONDS, J. P. and BRANDES, W. W. (1929). Effect of peptone upon hepatic veins in dog. *J. Pharmacol.* **35**, 165–170.

SIMPSON, A. M., EZROW, L. and SAPIRSTEIN, L. A. (1954). Measurement of plasma volume with rose bengal. *Amer. J. Physiol.* **177**, 319–324.

SJÖSTRAND, T. (1934). Funktionieren die leber und die lunge als Blutdepots? *Klin. Wscher.* **13**, 169–173.

SMYTHE, C. MCC. (1959). Effect of haemorrhage on hepatic blood flow determined by radioactive colloidal chromic phosphate removal. *Circulation Res.* **7**, 268–271.

SMYTHE, C. MCC., FITZPATRICK, H. F. and BLAKEMORE, A. H. (1951). Studies on portal venous oxygen content in unanaesthetized man. *J. clin. Invest.* **30**, 674.

SMYTHE, C. MCC., GILMORE, J. P. and HANDFORD, S. W. (1954). Effect of levarterenol (1-norepinephrine) on hepatic blood flow in normal, anaesthetized dog. *J. Pharmacol.* **110**, 398–402.

SMYTHE, C. MCC., HEINEMANN, H. O. and BRADLEY, S. E. (1953). Estimated hepatic blood flow in the dog. *Amer. J. Physiol.* **172**, 737–742.

SNOOK, T. (1950). A comparative study of the vascular compartments in mammalian spleens. *Amer. J. Anat.* **87**, 31–77.

SOSKIN, S., ESSEX, H. E., HERRICK, J. F. and MANN, F. C. (1938). Mechanism of regulation of blood sugar by the liver. *Amer. J. Physiol.* **124**, 558–567.

SPARROW, R. (1932). Neuere Befunde uber die Blutwege der Darmwand und ihre functionelle Bedeutung. *Morph. Jb.* **69**, 394–454.

STEINER, S. S. and MUELLER, C. E. (1961). Distribution of blood flow in the digestive tract of the rat. *Circulation Res.* **14**, 99–102.

STUKELEY, W. (1723). *On the Spleen, its Description and History, Use and Disease.* London.

TARCHANOFF, P. I. (1874). Ueber die Innervation der Milz und deren Beziehung zur leucocychamie. *Pflugers Arch.* **8**, 97–100.

TEXTER, E. C., MERRIL, S., SCHWARTZ, M., VANDERSTEPPEN, G. and HADDY, F. J. (1962). Relationship of blood flow to pressure in the intestinal vascular bed of the dog. *Amer. J. Physiol.* **202**, 253–256.

THAMM, M. (1940). Die portocavalen Venenberbindungen des Menschen. *Zbl. Chir.* **67**, 1828–1841.

THELEN, P. (1933). Zur Frage der Blutzuckeregulation durch Reflexe vom sinus caroticus. *Z. ges. exp. Med.* **86**, 231–243.

THOMAS, W. D. and ESSEX, H. E. (1949). Observations on the hepatic venous circulation with special reference to the sphincter mechanism. *Amer. J. Physiol.* **158**, 303–310.

THOMPSON, W. P., CAUGHEY, L. L., WHIPPLE, A. O. and ROSSELOT, L. M. (1937). Splenic vein pressure and congestive splenomegaly (Bantis syndrome). *J. clin. Invest.* **16**, 571–572.

TORRANCE, H. B. (1961). The control of the hepatic arterial circulation. *J. Physiol.* **158**, 39–49.

TOURNADE, A. (1930). Le sinus carotidien et le nerf de Hering. Leur rôle dans le fonctionnement de l'appareil cardio-vasculaire. *Lyon Med.* **146**, 97–110.

TRAPOLD, J. H. (1956). Effect of ganglionic blocking agents upon blood flow and resistance in the superior mesenteric artery of the dog. *Circulation Res.* **4**, 718–723.

TROWELL, O. A. (1946). The experimental production of watery vacuolation of the liver. *J. Physiol.* **105**, 268–297.

UTTERBACK, R. A. (1944). The innervation of the spleen. *J. comp. Neurol.* **81**, 55–66.

VAIREL, J. (1933). Action de l'adrenaline et de l'acetylcholine sur la rate. *J. Physiol. Path. gen.* **31**, 42–52.

VOLKMANN, J. (1923). Zur chirurgischen Anatomie der Milzgefasse. *Zbl. Chir.* nr **11**.

WADE, O. L., COMBES, B., CHILDS, A. W., WHEELER, H. O., COURNARD, O. and BRADLEY, S. E. (1956). The effect of exercise on the splanchnic blood flow and splanchnic blood volume in normal man. *Clin. Sci.* **15**, 457–463.

WAGNER, R. (1849). Nachstehende Untersuchungen uber die Kontractilitat der Milz vorgelegt. *Nach. Ges. Wiss. (Gottingen)*, pp. 89–96.

WAKIM, K. G. (1944). The effect of certain substances on the intrahepatic circulation of blood in the intact animal. *Amer. Heart J.* **27**, 289–300.

— (1954). Physiology of the liver. *Amer. J. Med.* **16**, 256–271.

WAKIM, K. G. and MANN, F. C. (1942). The intrahepatic circulation of the blood. *Anat. Rec.* **82**, 233–253.

WALDER, D. N. (1952). Arteriovenous anastomoses of the human stomach. *Clin. Sci.* **11**, 59–71.

— (1954). Vascularization of stomach in relation to aetiology of peptic ulcer. *Gastroenterology.* **81**, 66–71.

WALKER, R. M. (1961). Surgical physiology of the liver. *J. Oslo City Hosp.* **11**, 109–110.

WASSERMAN, A. J. and PATTERSON, J. L. (1961). The cerebral vascular response to reduction in arterial carbon dioxide tension. *J. clin. Invest.* **40**, 1297–1303.

WASSERMAN, F. (1958). The structure of the wall of the hepatic sinusoids in the electron microscope. *Z. Zellforsch.* **49**, 13–21.

WEIDENREICH, F. (1901). Das Gefassystem der menschlichen Milz. *Arch. mikr. Anat.* **58**, 347–376.

WEISS, L. (1963). The structure of intermediate vascular pathways in the spleen of rabbits. *Amer. J. Anat.* **113**, 51–92.

WELCH, G. E., EMMETT, R., CRAIGHEAD, C. C., HOEFFLER, G., BROWNE, D. C. and ROSEN, I. (1954). Simultaneous pressure measurements in the hepatic venule and portal venous system in man. *Amer. J. med. Sci.* **228**, 643–645.

WERNER, A. Y. and HORVATH, S. M. (1952). Measurement of the intrahepatic blood flow in the dog, by the bromsulphalein method. *J. clin. Invest.* **31**, 433–439.

WERNER, A. Y., MACCANON, D. M. and HORVATH, S. M. (1952). Fractional distribution of total blood flow to and oxygen consumption of the liver as influenced by mild haemorrhage. *Amer. J. Physiol.* **170**, 624–630.

WHITE, B., COBB, S. and JONES, L. (1939). Mucous colitis. In *Psychosomatic Medicine*. New York: Nat. Res. Council Monograph No. 1, 18–21.

WHITTAKER, S. R. F. and WINTON, R. F. (1933). The apparent viscosity of blood flowing in the isolated hind limb of the dog and its variation with corpuscular concentration. *J. Physiol.* **78**, 339–369.

WIGGERS, C. J. (1950). *The Physiology of Shock*. New York: Commonwealth Fund.

WIGGERS, C. J., OPDYKE, D. F. and JOHNSON, J. R. (1946). Portal pressure gradient under experimental conditions, including haemorrhagic shock. *Amer. J. Physiol.* **146**, 192–206.

WILKINS, R. W., CULBERTSON, J. W. and INGLEFINGER, F. J. (1951). The effect of splanchnic sympathectomy in hypertensive patients upon estimated hepatic blood flow in the upright as contrasted with the horizontal position. *J. clin. Invest.* **30**, 312–317.

WILSON, J. W. (1958). Liver structure in relation to liver function. In *Liver Function*. Ed. Brauer, R. W. Amer. Inst. Biol. Sci. Monograph No. 4, 175–189.

WOLF, S. and WOLFF, A. G. (1943). *Human Gastric Function*. New York: Oxford Univ. Press.

WYATT, D. G. (1961). Problems in the measurement of blood flow by magnetic induction. *Physics in Med. Biol.* **5**, 289–320; 369–399.

ZWEIFACH, B. W. (1949). Basic mechanisms in peripheral vascular homeostasis. In factors regulating blood pressure. Trans. of 3rd Conference Josiah Macy Jr. Foundation. Ed. Zweifach, B. W., and Shorr, E. New York: pp. 13–52.

ZWEIFACH, B. W., LEE, R. E., HYMAN, C. and CHAMBERS, R. (1944). Omental circulation in morphinized dogs subjected to graded haemorrhage. *Ann. Surg.* **120**, 232–250.

ZWEIFACH, B. W., LOWENSTEIN, B. E. and CHAMBERS, R. (1944). Responses of blood capillaries to acute haemorrhage in the rat. *Amer. J. Physiol.* **142**, 80–93.

INDEX